STRUCTURAL PRINCIPLES IN
INORGANIC COMPOUNDS

STRUCTURAL PRINCIPLES IN
INORGANIC COMPOUNDS

W. E. ADDISON, Ph.D.
Lecturer in Chemistry, University of Nottingham

LONGMANS

LONGMANS, GREEN AND CO LTD
48 GROSVENOR STREET, LONDON W I

*Associated companies, branches and representatives
throughout the world*

FIRST PUBLISHED 1961
SECOND IMPRESSION 1962
THIRD IMPRESSION 1963
FOURTH IMPRESSION 1963
FIFTH IMPRESSION 1965

PRINTED IN GREAT BRITAIN BY
T. AND A. CONSTABLE LTD, EDINBURGH

PREFACE

The direct correlation of the physical properties and chemical reactions of elements and compounds with the way in which their constituent atoms are arranged in space has become increasingly appreciated in recent years. A picture of atomic structure often facilitates chemical thought.

This book is concerned primarily with the structure of elements and compounds, and attempts to pick out some of the underlying principles by the description of a selected number of examples. It does not attempt to be comprehensive, but it is hoped that a student who has used it will feel able to work out for himself a likely structure for any known material which he encounters.

An attempt has been made to treat the subject-matter at an elementary level, and it is based on a lecture course given by the author to first-year classes at Nottingham University during the past six years.

Since structure follows from chemical bonding, the first chapter discusses the electronic theory of the atom, the different types of chemical bond, and features associated with them. Examples of structure are discussed according to the nature of the bonding and according to whether a substance comprises discrete molecules or has an infinite three-dimensional lattice. Electron pair repulsions and ligand field theory are used in discussing the former, whereas the fundamental importance of close packed arrangements is emphasized in discussing the latter. In addition, brief chapters have been included to discuss the defect solid state and the methods which are used in the determination of structure.

The account of these various topics has been made as concise as possible as it is intended that the student should be encouraged to develop the ideas for himself. Reference is made to a number of texts suitable for further pursuit of the subject.

The author wishes to express his sincere thanks to his colleagues, Professor C. C. Addison, Dr. N. N. Greenwood, Dr. S. C. Wallwork, and Dr. J. B. Raynor for much helpful comment and advice, and to his wife for her understanding and assistance at every stage in the preparation of the book.

W. ERIC ADDISON

CONTENTS

1

ELECTRONIC THEORY OF THE
ATOM AND CHEMICAL BONDING

Introduction

The advances in physical techniques of the last forty years have afforded much information about the arrangements of atoms in space, i.e. the structure of elements and compounds. It is now general practice to study inorganic compounds under the three headings of preparation, properties and structure instead of under the first two only as formerly. Knowledge of structure has advanced far since the optical activity of carbon compounds was attributed to a tetrahedral distribution of bonds from a carbon atom, and the properties of aromatic compounds to a planar ring with bond angles of 120° in the benzene molecule.

Some account will be given in the following chapters of the structures of the elements and of some simple inorganic compounds to illustrate the underlying principles which govern the arrangement of atoms in space.

It can be appreciated that when atoms are built into a crystal lattice, they approach each other closely and this close approach leads to an interaction between adjacent atoms and particularly the outermost parts of these atoms, the electrons. This interaction of electrons is the formation of chemical bonds. Before considering the structures of elements and compounds, the electronic configurations of the elements and the various types of chemical bond must be described.

The Electronic Theory of the Atom

Since theories of electronic structure are comprehensively treated in text-books of physical chemistry, no detailed treatment of them will be given here although some of the results will be discussed. The theory of Rutherford and Bohr which was put forward in 1913 postulated that electrons revolve round the nucleus of an atom in fixed orbits and that each orbit corresponds to a definite amount of energy; no energy is gained or lost as the electrons rotate round the nucleus, but there is an energy change associated with the moving of an electron from one orbit to another. When energy is supplied to an atom, an electron can move to an orbit of higher energy, usually regarded as being further from the nucleus, and this same amount of energy is given out when the electron falls back to its original orbit.

It followed from developments of this theory that each electron in an atom is characterised by four numbers known as quantum numbers, the term quantum implying that a definite amount of energy is involved. These quantum numbers, called respectively Principal, Azimuthal, Magnetic and Spin, have certain permitted values and these are indicated in Table I.

TABLE I

Quantum Number	Symbol	Range of permitted Values
Principal	n	$1, 2, 3, \ldots n$
Azimuthal	l^*	$0, 1, 2, \ldots (n-1)$
Magnetic	m_l	$l, (l-1) \ldots 0 \ldots (-l)$
Spin	m_s	$\pm \frac{1}{2}$

If the principal quantum number n has the value of 1, then in accordance with Table I the only value possible for both the azimuthal quantum number l and the magnetic quantum number m_l is 0. The spin quantum number m_s can have the values of $+\frac{1}{2}$ and $-\frac{1}{2}$, and so there are only two possible combinations of quantum numbers when the principal quantum number has the value of 1, as shown below in Table II.

TABLE II

n	l	m_l	m_s
1	0	0	$+\frac{1}{2}$
1	0	0	$-\frac{1}{2}$

If the principal quantum number has the value of 2, the azimuthal quantum number can have values of 0 and 1, and the different combinations of the quantum numbers which are possible are given in Table III.

There are thus eight possible combinations of the four quantum numbers when the principal quantum number has a value of 2, two of these corresponding to a value of 0 for the azimuthal quantum number and six of these to the value of 1.

When the principal quantum number has a value of 3, the azimuthal quantum number can have the values of 0, 1 and 2. The number of combinations for the values of 0 and 1 are again two and six as in Table III. When the azimuthal quantum number has the value of 2, the magnetic

---

* This quantum number was originally denoted by the symbol k, and the values of k were $1, 2, 3, \ldots n$.

quantum number can have five different values, 2, 1, 0, −1, −2, and for each of these the spin quantum number can be $+\frac{1}{2}$ or $-\frac{1}{2}$, making ten combinations in all. This can be summarised as follows:

$$n=3 \quad l=0 \quad \text{2 possible combinations}$$
$$l=1 \quad \text{6 possible combinations}$$
$$l=2 \quad \text{10 possible combinations}$$
$$\text{—}$$
$$\text{Total} \quad \text{18 possible combinations}$$

There are thus eighteen possible combinations of the four quantum numbers when the principal quantum number has a value of 3. It can be seen by making a similar calculation that when the principal quantum number has a value of 4, the number of possible combinations of the four quantum numbers is $2+6+10+14=32$.

TABLE III

n	l	m_l	m_s
2	0	0	$+\frac{1}{2}$
2	0	0	$-\frac{1}{2}$
2	1	1	$+\frac{1}{2}$
2	1	0	$+\frac{1}{2}$
2	1	−1	$+\frac{1}{2}$
2	1	1	$-\frac{1}{2}$
2	1	0	$-\frac{1}{2}$
2	1	−1	$-\frac{1}{2}$

In any one atom no two electrons can have the same values for all four quantum numbers. Hence the numbers of possible combinations of quantum numbers, i.e. 2, 8, 18 and 32, which correspond to the values of the principal quantum number of 1, 2, 3 and 4, are also the numbers of electrons which can occupy the various 'shells' surrounding atomic nuclei. These numbers are also the numbers of elements found in the various periods of the Periodic Table, although the correlation is not precise since these periods contain successively 2, 8, 8, 18, 18 and 32 elements. This point will be considered further below, p. 6.

There are conventions used in describing electrons. Thus all the electrons which have the same principal quantum number are said to constitute a 'shell', and when $n=1, 2, 3, 4, \ldots$ these are known as the K, L, M, $N \ldots$ shells. The K shell can contain two electrons, the L shell eight electrons, the M shell eighteen electrons and the N shell thirty-two electrons. When the azimuthal quantum number has values of 0, 1, 2, 3, . . . the electrons are referred to as s, p, d, f . . . electrons. (These letters are abbreviations of spectroscopic terms and stand for sharp, principal, diffuse and fundamental respectively.)

The results which were obtained above can be expressed more concisely by stating that the K shell can contain two s electrons, the L shell two s and six p electrons, the M shell two s, six p and ten d electrons, and the N shell two s electrons, six p electrons, ten d electrons and fourteen f electrons. This notation will be used throughout and it is important that the student should be familiar with it.

Each electron possesses a definite amount of energy. When electrons in an isolated atom have the same principal quantum number and the same azimuthal quantum number, they do not differ in energy, but electrons which differ either in the principal or in the azimuthal quantum number have appreciably different energies. The electrons of lowest energy are the 1s electrons, i.e. those which have a principal quantum number of 1 and an azimuthal quantum number of 0; since the two 1s electrons have the same energy this is sometimes referred to as the 1s (energy) level. Next in order of increasing energy is the 2s level followed by the 2p level and so on; it is necessary to be familiar with the sequence in which the first eighteen energy levels are filled as the atomic number of the elements increases, and this is as follows:

$$1s, \ 2s, \ 2p, \ 3s, \ 3p, \ 4s, \ 3d, \ 4p, \ 5s, \ 4d, \ 5p, \ 6s, \ 4f, \ 5d, \ 6p, \ 7s, \ 6d \approx 5f.$$

The above sequence is the arrangement of the energy levels in order of increase in the value of $(n+l)$, where n is the numerical value of the principal and l that of the azimuthal quantum number. When two levels have the same value of $(n+l)$, that with the lower value of n comes first.

This sequence can also be remembered easily if the levels are written down as in Fig. 1. The possible sub-levels in the various shells are arranged in horizontal lines, and the correct sequence is then obtained by following the eight successive diagonals drawn in the Figure from right to left.

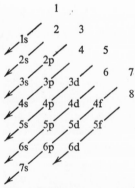

FIG. 1 The sequence in which atomic energy levels are occupied.

The Periodic Table

The elements in the Periodic Table are arranged in order of increasing atomic number. Since the atomic number of an element is defined as the number of protons in the nucleus of each atom of that element and the positively charged protons are balanced electrically by an equal number of negatively charged extranuclear electrons, it follows that elements are built up in such a way that an atom of one element contains one more electron than an atom of the preceeding element. Electrons normally occupy the lowest energy level available to them and the levels are filled in the sequence given above. With this knowledge of the sequence of energy levels and of the number of electrons which are required to fill each level, it is possible to write the electronic configurations of the various elements.

The first element, hydrogen, has an atomic number of 1, and therefore it has one electron which must be in the lowest energy level, the $1s$ level. Thus the electronic configuration of hydrogen is written as $1s^1$, the superscript denoting the number of electrons in the particular level. Helium, with atomic number 2, has the electronic configuration $1s^2$ and this represents a complete K shell, since the K shell can contain only s electrons and there can be only two s electrons in any one shell.

In lithium, with atomic number 3, there is a complete K shell and the third electron must be in the next energy level, the $2s$ level; the configuration can be written as $1s^2 2s^1$, or $K2s^1$, where K denotes a complete shell. From boron, with atomic number 5, to neon with atomic number 10, the L shell is being filled and the electronic configurations of the various elements are as follows:

Lithium	$K2s^1$	Boron	$K2s^2 2p^1$	Oxygen	$K2s^2 2p^4$
Beryllium	$K2s^2$	Carbon	$K2s^2 2p^2$	Fluorine	$K2s^2 2p^5$
		Nitrogen	$K2s^2 2p^3$	Neon	$K2s^2 2p^6$ (or KL).

From the next element sodium, with atomic number 11, to argon with atomic number 18, the $3s$ and the $3p$ levels are filled in the same way as were the $2s$ and $2p$ levels so that argon has the electronic configuration $KL3s^2 3p^6$. The M shell is not complete at argon however, since there is also a $3d$ level, but this is unoccupied in argon. It was seen above that the $4s$ level is of lower energy than the $3d$ level and so electrons will occupy the $4s$ level before the $3d$ level. Potassium and calcium, with atomic numbers 19 and 20 respectively, have the electronic configurations $KL3s^2 3p^6 4s^1$ and $KL3s^2 3p^6 4s^2$; and then from the next element scandium, with atomic number 21, to zinc, with atomic number 30, the $3d$ level is filled so that zinc has the electronic configuration $KL3s^23p^63d^{10}4s^2$, or $KLM4s^2$ (since the filling of the $3d$ level completes the M shell). The $4p$ level is then filled and is complete at krypton, $KLM4s^24p^6$. It should be noted that the elements from scandium to zinc, i.e. when the $3d$ level is being filled, have electrons of a higher principal quantum number also, i.e. the $4s$ electrons. This has a significant effect upon the chemical properties of the elements, and a similar situation is found when the other d and f levels are being filled. The electronic configurations of all the elements are given in the Appendix, p. 168.

The Periodic Table is illustrated on p. 8 in its long form. The electronic configurations of the elements can be written down by reference to this Table since the various portions of it correspond to filling different levels, and this is illustrated in Fig. 2, which should be compared with the Periodic Table to illustrate the point.

		$1s$
$2s$		$2p$
$3s$		$3p$
$4s$	$3d$	$4p$
$5s$	$4d$	$5p$
$6s$	$4f$ and $5d$	$6p$
$7s$	$(6d, 5f)$	

FIG. 2 The framework of the Periodic
Table, showing energy levels only.

It can be seen that it is the sequence in which the various energy levels are filled which determines the number of elements in each period of the Periodic Table, each period being completed when a p level is completed (except that which contains only hydrogen and helium). The various periods contain successively 2, 8, 8, 18, 18, 32, ? elements.

It can be seen from Fig. 2 that, omitting the $1s$ level, the Periodic Table can be divided into four regions according to whether the elements are filling up s, p, d or f levels; in general, the chemical properties of an element are characterised by the region in which it is situated. Each s block element is a strongly electropositive metal which gives colourless ions in solution, and which exists in the same oxidation state in almost all its compounds.* Most p block elements are non-metals, whereas such

---

* The term oxidation state is preferred to the term valency. It can de befined as the number of electrons which have to be added (to a cation) or removed (from an anion) in order to produce an electrically neutral atom after the atoms of the compound concerned have been separated from each other as normal ions, i.e. N^{3-}, O^{2-}, Cl^-, etc. Consider two examples to illustrate this. Firstly the ferrous ion; the iron bears a positive charge of $+2$, and so two electrons must be added to produce a neutral atom;

metallic elements as occur therein are perhaps not truly metallic, e.g. arsenic and antimony; they form two series of compounds in which the metal exists in different oxidation states represented as N and $(N-2)$, where N is the number of the group in the Periodic Table in which the element occurs. The d block elements, referred to as the Transition Elements since they are situated between the s and p blocks, are metals which usually form coloured ions and which in most cases form several series of compounds in which the metal exists in different oxidation states (e.g. chromium forms well-known series of compounds in which it has the oxidation states $+2$, $+3$ and $+6$); moreover, these oxidation states can differ from each other by one unit and not always by two units as in the p block elements. The f block comprises the lanthanide and transuranium series of metals whose members are characterised by having great similarity in all their properties to their immediate neighbours within the block. From this it can be seen that the electronic configuration of an element is related to the chemical nature of the element, and its importance in understanding chemical bonding will be seen in later sections.

Modern Atomic Theory

An attempt must now be made to describe the results of modern atomic theory but without giving the mathematics used in their derivation. Whereas in the earlier theory it was considered that electrons revolved round the nucleus in circular and elliptical orbits which were planar, modern theory describes an electron in terms of probability and is unable to define a sharp path for it. The term orbit is replaced by the term orbital, and each orbital in an atom can contain two electrons which differ from each other only in their spin quantum numbers. (An orbital is a solution to a complicated mathematical equation.)

Theoretical calculations are most precise for a hydrogen atom, which is the simplest system possible as it contains only one extranuclear electron. It must be appreciated that whereas the electron in a hydrogen atom

hence the iron has an oxidation state of $+2$. (Similarly in potassium ferrocyanide, $K_4Fe(CN)_6$, where the potassiums are removed with a charge of $+1$ and the cyanides with a charge of -1 leaving the iron as $+2$ for the whole to be electrically neutral.) Secondly, the ion NO_3^-; the composite ion has an oxidation state of -1 since an electron has to be removed to produce a neutral entity. Next consider the atoms individually; when a covalent bond is formed it is assumed for the purpose of defining the oxidation state that the electrons are gained by the more electronegative atom (p. 21); in this case each oxygen atom is separated with the two electrons and hence a charge of -2, making a total charge of -6; the nitrogen atom must have an oxidation state of $+5$ to leave a net charge of -1 on the ion. The nitrogen atom is bonded to three oxygen atoms and is sometimes described as tervalent. None the less, the nitrogen atom forms our bonds (three σ and one π, see p. 103) and so might be described as four-valent; it has a coordination number of three (p. 44). The term oxidation state, i.e. $+5$ for the nitrogen atom in this case, avoids any ambiguity.

PERIODIC TABLE

Groups Period	1	2												3	4	5	6	7	0	Inert gas electronic configurations
1																		$_1$H	$_2$He	2
2	$_3$Li	$_4$Be												$_5$B	$_6$C	$_7$N	$_8$O	$_9$F	$_{10}$Ne	2, 8
3	$_{11}$Na	$_{12}$Mg												$_{13}$Al	$_{14}$Si	$_{15}$P	$_{16}$S	$_{17}$Cl	$_{18}$Ar	2, 8, 8
4	$_{19}$K	$_{20}$Ca	$_{21}$Sc	$_{22}$Ti	$_{23}$V	$_{24}$Cr	$_{25}$Mn	$_{26}$Fe	$_{27}$Co	$_{28}$Ni	$_{29}$Cu	$_{30}$Zn		$_{31}$Ga	$_{32}$Ge	$_{33}$As	$_{34}$Se	$_{35}$Br	$_{36}$Kr	2, 8, 18, 8
5	$_{37}$Rb	$_{38}$Sr	$_{39}$Y	$_{40}$Zr	$_{41}$Nb	$_{42}$Mo	$_{43}$Tc	$_{44}$Ru	$_{45}$Rh	$_{46}$Pd	$_{47}$Ag	$_{48}$Cd		$_{49}$In	$_{50}$Sn	$_{51}$Sb	$_{52}$Te	$_{53}$I	$_{54}$Xe	2, 8, 18, 18, 8
6	$_{55}$Cs	$_{56}$Ba	$_{57}$La etc.	$_{72}$Hf	$_{73}$Ta	$_{74}$W	$_{75}$Re	$_{76}$Os	$_{77}$Ir	$_{78}$Pt	$_{79}$Au	$_{80}$Hg		$_{81}$Tl	$_{82}$Pb	$_{83}$Bi	$_{84}$Po	$_{85}$At	$_{86}$Rn	2, 8, 18, 32, 18, 8
7	$_{87}$Fr	$_{88}$Ra	$_{89}$Ac	$_{90}$Th	$_{91}$Pa	$_{92}$U														

Lanthanides	$_{58}$Ce	$_{59}$Pr	$_{60}$Nd	$_{61}$Pm	$_{62}$Sm	$_{63}$Eu	$_{64}$Gd	$_{65}$Tb	$_{66}$Dy	$_{67}$Ho	$_{68}$Er	$_{69}$Tm	$_{70}$Yb	$_{71}$Lu
Transuranium elements		$_{93}$Np	$_{94}$Pu	$_{95}$Am	$_{96}$Cm	$_{97}$Bk	$_{98}$Cf	$_{99}$Es	$_{100}$Fm	$_{101}$Md	$_{102}$No			

normally occupies the $1s$ level, other levels occur also although these are of higher energy, and hence the electron can only occupy them if it is supplied with additional energy. When the electron is in the $1s$ level the atom is said to be in the electronic ground state, but when the electron has been promoted to a higher energy level the atom is in an excited state.

It is not possible to represent completely in one diagram the directional properties of an electron in an orbital of the hydrogen atom. Two separate representations must be given and these must be combined in the mind's eye to give an overall mental picture. These are (i) an angular probability distribution and (ii) a radial probability distribution. These will be considered in turn.

The angular probability distribution gives the probability of finding an electron in a particular direction. An s electron has no preferred direction in space, i.e. there is an equal chance of finding it in any direction with respect to the nucleus. A graphical representation of this is shown in Fig. 3; it can be considered that the nucleus of the atom is at the origin and the surface of the sphere represents the probability of finding the s electron, which is therefore the same in all directions.

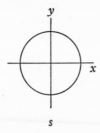

FIG. 3 The angular probability distribution of an s orbital: (only a cross-section through the sphere is shown).

It was seen on p. 4 that a p level can contain six electrons and thus there are three p orbitals corresponding to each value of the principal quantum number. These three orbitals are mutually at right angles and the three angular probability distributions are shaped like dumb-bells along the x, y and z axes as shown in Fig. 4 and hence the orbitals are referred to as p_x, p_y and p_z respectively. Thus in the p_x orbital it is most likely that the electron will be found in the direction of the x axis and there is no chance at all of it being found in either direction at right angles to the x axis, and similarly with the p_y and the p_z orbitals. Note that the lobes in Fig. 4 are not planar and a three-dimensional picture of

B

each function is obtained by rotating the two-dimensional representation about the appropriate axis.

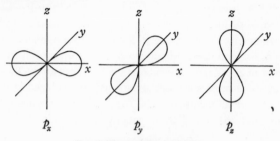

FIG. 4 The angular probability distributions of p orbitals.

The angular probability distributions of the five d orbitals are still more complicated and are shown in Fig. 5. In three of these the lobes lie between the axial directions and are named according to these directions d_{xy}, d_{yz} and d_{zx}. In one of the others, the $d_{x^2-y^2}$ orbital, the lobes correspond with the x and y axes, and in the remaining d_{z^2} orbital they correspond with the z axis. Hence the orbitals can be divided into two sets; in the one set there are two orbitals whose angular probability distributions are concentrated along the axial directions, whereas in the other set there are three orbitals whose angular probability distributions are at a maximum at 45° to the axial directions. Since f orbitals are of little importance in chemical bonding, they are not considered here.

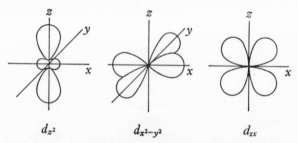

FIG. 5 The angular probability distributions of d orbitals: (those of the d_{yz} and d_{xy} orbitals resemble that of the d_{zx} orbital but are related to the appropriate axes).

It should be emphasised again that these figures do not illustrate orbitals, but do illustrate the probability of finding an electron in any direction. In each diagram the nucleus of the atom is considered to be at the origin, and the probability of finding the electron in any direction is proportional to the distance from the origin to the surface when a straight line is drawn in the appropriate direction.

The graphs of the angular probability which have been discussed above give no indication of the probable distance of an electron from the nucleus, but only of its most probable direction. The distance of an electron from the nucleus is given by the radial probability distribution. In Fig. 6 the probability of finding the electron at distance r from the nucleus is plotted against r for the 1s, 2s, 2p, 3s, 3p and 3d orbitals of the hydrogen atom. Three points should be noted. Firstly, in each case the probability is zero

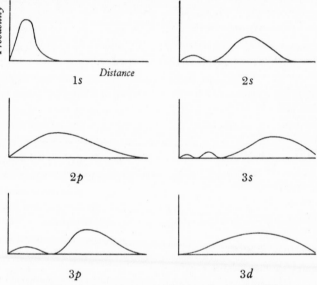

FIG. 6 The radial probability distributions for certain orbitals.

at the origin—the nucleus; secondly, the distributions vary according to the principal quantum number, so that the larger the value of the principal quantum number the further the electron is likely to be from the nucleus (in contrast to this, the angular probability distribution is unaffected by a change in the value of the principal quantum number). Thirdly, the value of r corresponding to the maximum probability in the graph of the 1s radial distribution agrees with the value calculated by Bohr for the distance of the circular orbit from the nucleus of the hydrogen atom.

To obtain a complete picture of the probability of finding the electron in any orbital the two distributions must be considered together, and the mpossibility of representing the composite probability distribution in two dimensions can be appreciated. Note again that none of these Figures is a diagram of an orbital.

So far the orbitals of a hydrogen atom with its single electron have been considered. For atoms with more than one electron calculation of the radial probability distribution becomes very difficult, but the angular probability distributions for *s*, *p*, *d* and *f* electrons remain the same to a first approximation as have been illustrated above for hydrogen. Hence it can be said that, provided the values of its quantum numbers are known, the probability of finding any electron in any atom in any direction in space—the angular probability—is known, but its probable distance from the nucleus of the atom cannot be calculated with precision. As was the case with the hydrogen atom, however, the radial probability distribution of all electrons falls off quite sharply with increase in distance from the nucleus after the maximum has been passed. An important consequence of this is that it is not possible to quote a definite value for the radius of an atom since there is a finite possibility, sometimes very small, that the outermost electrons of the atom can be found almost anywhere between the nucleus and infinity.

One further aspect of atomic theory which must be referred to is Hund's rule. It was seen above that a *p* level which can contain six electrons is divided into three orbitals so that each orbital can contain two electrons. Hund stated that no orbital will contain two electrons until each orbital in that energy level is occupied singly. This behaviour is found not only for *p* levels but also for *d* and *f* levels in the majority of cases.

The necessity of having a knowledge of electronic configurations and of the directional properties of atomic orbitals will become clear when examples are discussed in Chapters 5-7.

Types of Chemical Bond

Some consideration will now be given to the most important types of bond which hold together atoms in the solid state, but without giving a detailed theoretical treatment of them.

(1) The Metallic Bond

Solid metals can be regarded conveniently as comprising positively charged ions held together by negatively charged electrons which are free to move rapidly throughout the metal lattice. The positive and negative charges are balanced since the electrons originate in the neutral metal atoms, and the attractive force of the unlike charges balances the repulsive force of the like charges. Many physical properties of metals, e.g. conductivity, become understandable as a result of the mobility of these electrons.

(2) The Ionic Bond

The lack of chemical reactivity shown by the family of Inert Gases, i.e. helium, neon, argon, krypton, xenon and radon, is outstanding among the elements. With the exception of helium these have the electronic configuration ns^2np^6 in their outermost shell, and it was realised at an early stage in electronic theory that atoms of other elements would become more stable if they could achieve this configuration by the gain or loss of one or more electrons.

Consider potassium chloride, KCl. The electronic configurations of chlorine, argon and potassium are as follows:

$$Cl \quad KL3s^23p^5$$
$$Ar \quad KL3s^23p^6$$
$$K \quad KL3s^23p^64s^1$$

It can be seen that if the $4s$ electron is transferred from a potassium atom to a chlorine atom then both atoms will acquire the electronic configuration $KL3s^23p^6$, which is the configuration of the inert gas argon. In addition, the chlorine atom will gain a negative charge and the potassium atom, by losing a negatively charged electron, will gain a positive charge. These resultant charged species are called ions, the positively charged is a cation and the negatively charged an anion, and it can be appreciated that the unlike charges will be held together by electrostatic attraction. Thus a compound, potassium chloride, is obtained in which both atoms have acquired an inert gas type of electronic configuration with its consequent stability. The type of bond which holds the ions together is called an ionic bond (sometimes an electrovalent bond), and such compounds as contain ionic bonds are known as ionic compounds.

The ions in potassium chloride are formed by a transference of one electron, but in many cases more than one electron requires to be transferred. Thus aluminium, which has the electronic configuration $K2s^22p^63s^23p^1$, can lose three electrons to become $K2s^22p^6$ (or KL) and form an ion Al^{3+}, while oxygen, which has the electronic configuration $K2s^22p^4$, can gain two electrons to become $K2s^22p^6$ and form the O^{2-} ion. Both these ions have the neon configuration. For the compound aluminium oxide to be electrically neutral the elements require to combine in the ratio of two aluminium atoms to three oxygen atoms, i.e. Al_2O_3.

Although in many ionic compounds the ions have the electronic configurations of inert gases, this is not always so. In particular, the transition metals form ions which do not have inert gas type of configurations, although these ions differ only in possessing some additional d electrons in excess of the configuration ns^2np^6. The configurations of some transition metals and some common ions derived from them are shown below to illustrate this.

Cr	$KL3s^23p^63d^54s^1$	Cr^{3+}	$KL3s^23p^63d^3$
Fe	$KL3s^23p^63d^64s^2$	Fe^{2+}	$KL3s^23p^63d^6$
		Fe^{3+}	$KL3s^23p^63d^5$
Cu	$KL3s^23p^63d^{10}4s^1$	Cu^+	$KL3s^23p^63d^{10}$
		Cu^{2+}	$KL3s^23p^63d^9$

In relatively few cases are cations known which do not have complete s and p levels in their outermost shell. Examples are Tl^+ and Pb^{2+} which both have the electronic configuration $KLMN5s^25p^65d^{10}6s^2$.

It is more important for the formation of an ionic compound that it should be energetically favourable than that an inert gas type of configuration should result and this will be considered in detail later, p. 16. It should be noted that ions which have odd numbers of s or p electrons are not known, although the examples given above show that an odd number of d electrons is found in many cases.

(3) The Covalent Bond

When an ionic bond is formed there is a transference of one or more electrons from one atom to another, with the formation of inert gas configurations for the constituent atoms in many cases, whereas when a covalent bond is formed between two atoms each atom contributes one electron and the electrons are shared between both atoms. As with the ionic bond, the atoms could be said to have acquired inert gas configurations in many cases, although it must be remembered that since some of the electrons are shared the atoms do not have complete control of the same number of electrons as has the appropriate inert gas atom.

Consider the chlorine molecule, Cl_2. The electronic configuration of a chlorine atom is $KL3s^23p^5$, so that it has seven electrons in its outermost shell and is only one short of the configuration of the inert gas argon which is $KL3s^23p^6$. The chlorine atoms can acquire the eight electrons (sometimes referred to as an octet) of the argon configuration only if they share two electrons between them, when each atom possesses six electrons completely and has a half share of two more, but remains uncharged since the neutral atom has seven electrons in its outermost shell and the bonded atom has six and two halves. Although there are no electrostatic forces, the atoms are held together by mutual interaction of the pair of electrons; this is a covalent bond. Whereas in the chlorine molecule each atom forms only one covalent bond, compounds are known where one atom forms as many as eight covalent bonds.

Although octets often result from covalent bond formation there are exceptions, and two of these will illustrate this point. Boron has the electronic configuration $K2s^22p^1$ and in the compound boron trifluoride, BF_3, it forms only three covalent bonds and so gains three shared electrons, making a total of six in its outermost shell, which is still two short of the neon configuration $2s^22p^6$. Again, sulphur has the electronic configuration $KL3s^23p^4$ and in the compound sulphur hexafluoride, SF_6, it forms six covalent bonds and so gains six shared electrons, making a total of twelve, which is four more than the number required to reach the argon configuration $KL3s^23p^6$. More important perhaps than the gaining of octets is the fact that, as in ionic compounds, the covalently bonded atoms almost invariably have even numbers of both s and p electrons. The most important exceptions are some of the oxides of nitrogen and chlorine.

Since a covalent bond is formed by the interaction of electrons from two different atoms it is logical to assume that the atoms should approach each other in such an orientation that the orbitals containing the electrons can overlap with each other. It follows that when one atom forms several covalent bonds the angle between these bonds will be influenced by the directional properties of the orbitals occupied by the electrons, (see Hybridisation, Chapter 5). This is an important difference between covalent and ionic compounds and will be developed further in later chapters.

(4) The Coordinate, or Dative Covalent Bond

The occurrence and nature of this bond are implied in the alternative names used for it. It is found most frequently in coordination compounds (complexes) and is a covalent bond in which both electrons are provided (i.e. given) by the same atom. By analogy with the ionic bond (p. 13) this would be expected to produce electrical charges on both atoms, but this would be so only if the electron pair which constitutes the bond were equally shared between the two atoms. It is usually found that the atom which provides the two electrons and thereby acquires a formal positive charge is a strongly electronegative atom (see p. 21) such as oxygen or nitrogen, with the result that on average the electrons are nearer to it than to the other less electronegative atom. By this means the separation of charges is considerably reduced and the similarity to an ionic bond is also diminished. From most points of view the bond is identical to an ordinary covalent bond and no attempt will be made to differentiate between them in subsequent chapters.

In addition to the various types of bond described above there are weaker bonds known as van der Waals' forces, which hold molecules together in the solid state, but these are of little importance within the scope of this book.

The most important bonds are the ionic and the covalent (including dative covalent); the essential difference between them is that in the former one or more electrons are transferred completely from one atom to another, whereas in the latter two electrons are shared equally or unequally between two atoms. It will be useful to find out what factors influence bond type, and this can be done conveniently by considering the energetics of the formation of sodium chloride which is a typical ionic compound.

Energetics of Formation of Sodium Chloride

The standard heat of formation of solid sodium chloride is the heat given out when one gram molecule is formed from solid sodium and gaseous chlorine. This has been measured experimentally and is 98·2 K. cals. It is possible to proceed from the same starting materials to the same product by a series of steps where the energy of each step is known, and in accordance with Hess's law the energies involved in the two routes by which the final product is obtained can be equated to each other.

Consider this step-wise route from solid sodium and gaseous chlorine to solid sodium chloride. The first step is the conversion of sodium from the solid to the gaseous state in which it exists as sodium atoms, the energy required being the energy of sublimation, S. The second step is the removal of the outermost electron from each gaseous sodium atom to form gaseous sodium ions, the energy required being the Ionisation Potential, I. The third step is the dissociation of the chlorine molecules to give gaseous chlorine atoms, the energy required being the Dissociation Energy, D. (Since one gram molecule of NaCl is being considered, only one gram atom of chlorine is required, so the value used in the cycle below is $D/2$ as the dissociation energy produces two gram atoms of chlorine from one gram molecule.) The fourth step is the addition of an electron to each gaseous chlorine atom to form gaseous chlorine ions;

in contrast to the previous steps, energy is given out in this process, and this is known as the Electron Affinity, E. The final step is the formation of solid sodium chloride from the gaseous ions, and again energy is given out; this is known as the Lattice Energy, U. These processes are shown diagrammatically below as a cycle with the energies involved expressed in K. cals.

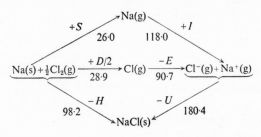

(By convention a + sign denotes that energy is supplied to the system and a − sign that energy is given out.)

A cycle of this type can be constructed for any compound; when applied to other compounds care must be used when introducing the electron affinity term, since this frequently involves an input of energy and not energy given out as in the above case (see below). If the energy of formation is large and the compound is exothermic, it is likely to be stable. It is clear from the magnitudes of the terms in the above cycle that the most important terms are the ionisation potential, the electron affinity and the lattice energy. An ionic compound is likely to be formed if the ionisation potential of the one element is relatively low, the electron affinity of the other element and the lattice energy of the compound as high as possible since these will all produce a large energy of formation. These three properties will now be considered in turn.

Ionisation Potential (see Appendix, p. 170)

It was seen on p. 1 that if sufficient energy is supplied to an electron it can be promoted to successively higher energy levels until finally it can be removed completely from the attractive force of the nucleus, leaving behind a positive ion. The energy required to do this is known as the ionisation potential and is defined as the energy required to remove an electron completely from a gaseous atom. It is usually measured in electron volts (where one electron volt (e.v.) is the energy gained by an electron falling through a potential difference of one volt, 1 e.v. $= 1 \cdot 6 \times 10^{-12}$

ergs), or in K.cals./g.mol. In considering chemical bonding it is the ionisation potentials of the outermost or valency electrons which are the most important.

Among the factors which influence the magnitude of the ionisation potential of an electron are:

(i) the distance of the electron from the nucleus;
(ii) the charge on the nucleus;
(iii) the screening effect of the other electrons of the atom.

The greater the distance of an electron from the positively charged nucleus, the weaker will be the attractive force and hence the lower the ionisation potential of that electron. The effect of distance is difficult to separate from the effect of nuclear charge since it is not possible for two atoms each in the ground state to have the same number of electrons at different distances from the nucleus. If, however, one atom is raised to an excited state by promoting one electron to a higher energy level, then that electron is further from the nucleus and it is found that it is more easily ionised than from the same atom in the ground state.

The greater the charge on the nucleus the more difficult it will be to remove an electron and hence the higher the value of the ionisation potential will be. In a vertical group of elements in the Periodic Table the distance of the valency electrons from the nucleus and the nuclear charge (i.e. number of protons in the nucleus) both increase with increasing atomic number, and these will have opposing effects upon the ionisation potential. In general, the effect of distance seems to be more important since the ionisation potential usually decreases with increase in atomic number within a vertical group. This trend is less marked, and indeed there are exceptions to it in the block of Transition elements. The values of the ionisation potential of the first electron for the alkali metals illustrate this trend. They are: lithium 5·4 e.v., sodium 5·1, potassium 4·3, rubidium 4·2 and caesium 3·9. These are among the lowest ionisation potentials of all the elements in the Periodic Table.

When the first ionisation potentials of the elements in a horizontal sequence are considered, the size of the atom decreases with increase in atomic number and the nuclear charge becomes successively greater. Both these factors lead to an increase in the ionisation potential of the outermost electron and the values for the first ionisation potentials of the elements of the first short period illustrate this increase. The values are: lithium 5·4, beryllium 9·3, boron 8·3, carbon 11·3, nitrogen 14·5, oxygen 13·6, fluorine 17·4, neon 21·6. The values for beryllium and nitrogen are slightly higher than would be expected from a comparison with the other elements, and these are attributed to the stability of a full s level and a half-filled p level respectively. In this series of elements the increase in nuclear charge is accompanied by an increase in the number of electrons. When, however, successive ionisation potentials of the same element are considered the nuclear charge becomes effectively greater since there are fewer electrons to screen it, and the result is a large increase in successive ionisation potentials as the values quoted below for magnesium and carbon show.

Magnesium	7·6	15·0	80·1		
Carbon	11·3	24·4	47·9	64·5	392·0

As the outermost electrons are removed, those remaining are pulled nearer to the nucleus by the relatively greater nuclear charge, and so the distance factor, though it may be of less importance, must also be involved in the above series.

The values of the ionisation potentials of many transition metals are larger than would be expected, and this is attributed to d electrons being less efficient than s and p electrons at screening the nuclear charge from the outermost electrons of the atom. The effect of this will be considered below.

In each horizontal period of the Periodic Table, the inert gas has the highest value for the ionisation potential of its first electron, which is in accordance with their chemical inertness. The removal of two electrons from a magnesium atom leaves a magnesium ion which has the neon configuration, and the energy required to remove a third electron is greater than would be expected by comparison with the energies required for the removal of the first two electrons, and this again reflects the stability of the inert gas type of configuration. The values quoted above for the successive ionisation potentials of carbon illustrate the same point.

It was seen that a low ionisation potential favoured ionic bond formation. From the preceding section it can be seen that ionisation potentials decrease from right to left across a period and also from top to bottom in a group of the Periodic Table. It also follows that the smaller the number of electrons which are ionised, i.e. the lower the charge on the cation, the lower the total ionisation potential will be. When these trends are considered along with the stability of the configuration ns^2np^6 it becomes clear which elements are likely to become cations in ionic compounds.

Electron Affinity

This is defined as the energy given out when an electron is added to a gaseous atom to form an ion. It seems reasonable to expect that the energy given out in forming an anion, i.e. the electron affinity, would balance the energy which has to be expended to produce a cation, i.e. the ionisation potential. This is not the case, however, since energy has to be provided to add one electron to most atoms to form an anion. Adding a second electron to an ion which already bears one negative charge always requires an appreciable amount of energy because of the repulsive force of like charges. Only the halogens give out energy when they are converted to anions, and the amount of energy given out is small. The values are: fluorine 3·6 e.v., chlorine 3·8, bromine 3·6, iodine 3·2. In view of this, the term electron affinity is rather a misnomer. It was seen that a large value for the electron affinity of the electronegative atom would enhance the stability of an ionic compound, but only the halogens fulfil this condition.

An extension of the discussion applied to ionisation potentials above leads to the conclusion that the smaller the size of the atom and the greater the nuclear charge the more likely it is that the electron affinity will be exoergic (i.e. energy given out, cf. exothermic), and therefore favourable for ionic bond formation. It should also be remembered that the halogens are the only elements which require to gain one electron only to form an anion, and that the sum of electron affinities for all the other elements is always endoergic (cf. endothermic).

Lattice Energy

This is the energy given out when gaseous ions of opposite charge are brought together from infinity into a solid lattice to form 1 g.mol. of a compound. The lattice energy can be regarded as a gain in the potential energy of the system due to the attraction of unlike charges. A theoretical value for the lattice energy of a compound can be obtained from the equation:

$$U = \frac{e^2 z^2 NA}{r}\left(1 - \frac{1}{n}\right),$$

where U is the lattice energy

e is the charge on an electron

z is the highest common factor of the charges on the two ions

N is the Avogadro number

A is the Madelung constant, and is dependent on the geometry of the crystal lattice r   is the distance apart of the nuclei of two unlike ions

n   is an integer which approximately equals 10 and is determined empirically.

A very important feature of this equation is that if both ions are polyvalent the term z^2 ensures a large value for the lattice energy. Since a high value for the lattice energy will increase the energy of formation considerably, it would seem that large charges on both ions would be advantageous for the stability of ionic compounds. While this is true in some compounds, it is not always true since this gain in energy is in some way compensated by the increasing ionisation potentials of successive electrons of the one atom and the endoergic process of adding more than one electron to the other. Expressed in another way, if Hess's law is applied to the cycle quoted on p. 17, then

$$-H = I + S + D/2 - E - U,$$

and it can be seen that an increase in the value of U will increase the energy of formation, but this is offset by an increase in the value of I and a change of sign in the term E.

If a calculation is attempted to determine whether a given compound is likely to have an ionic lattice or not, values for I, S, D and E are usually readily available. To obtain a value for U, the lattice energy, a probable structure for the compound must be guessed (see Chapters 3 and 4) in order that the Madelung constant can be determined and a reasonable value for the interionic distance must be assumed. If the calculated heat of formation is strongly exothermic, an ionic lattice is to be expected. Otherwise the compound is likely to become exothermic by forming a completely different type of lattice, built of covalent bonds, and to which the above treatment is inapplicable since no ions occur in the lattice.

Electronegativity

The combined effect of ionisation potential and electron affinity on the ionic character of a bond between two atoms can be related to the difference in electronegativity of the two atoms. Electronegativity is a measure of the tendency of an atom to attract an electron towards itself and has been variously evaluated by different authors. The definition given by Mulliken is simple to appreciate and allows some understanding of the term. He equated electronegativity to the mean of the ionisation potential and electron affinity of the element, i.e. electronegativity $= (I + E)/2$.

The values for the electronegativities of the elements which are the most often quoted are those of Pauling. (These are derived differently and further information should be sought in 'The Nature of the Chemical Bond'.) Some of these values are quoted in Table IV.

It can be seen that the value of electronegativity falls with increase in atomic number within a group and decreases from right to left in a period of the Periodic Table (cf. ionisation potential) so that the halogens are the most electronegative group of elements and the alkali metals the least electronegative (or the most electropositive). If there is an appreciable difference in the electronegativity values of two elements a bond formed between them is likely to be ionic, but if the difference is small the bond is likely to be covalent.

TABLE IV

Some Electronegativity Values (after Pauling)

Hydrogen	2·1	Arsenic	2·0	Yttrium	1·3
Fluorine	4·0	Antimony	1·8	Beryllium	1·5
Chlorine	3·0	Carbon	2·5	Magnesium	1·2
Bromine	2·8	Silicon	1·8	Calcium	1·0
Iodine	2·4	Germanium	1·7	Strontium	1·0
Oxygen	3·5	Tin	1·7	Barium	0·9
Sulphur	2·5	Boron	2·0	Lithium	1·0
Selenium	2·4	Aluminium	1·5	Sodium	0·9
Tellurium	2·1	Titanium	1·6	Potassium	0·8
Nitrogen	3·0	Zirconium	1·6	Rubidium	0·8
Phosphorus	2·1	Scandium	1·3	Caesium	0·7

To summarise, it seems likely that a bond between two atoms will be ionic,

    (i) if the metal atom forms a low-charged cation and the energy required to remove the electron(s), i.e. ionisation potential(s), is small;

   (ii) if the metal atom is large, since this also favours a low value for the ionisation potential;

  (iii) if the metal ion has an inert gas type of configuration, since in such an ion there is the most efficient screening of the nuclear charge by the electrons and this also favours a low ionisation potential;

  (iv) if the non-metallic atom is small and gives rise to an anion of low charge, since these conditions make it more likely that the gain of electron(s) to form the anion should be an exoergic or weakly endoergic process.

In contrast, if the cation is small a closer approach of the two oppositely charged ions can result and this leads to a large value for the lattice energy; such a value is also enhanced by high charges on both ions and it was seen that a high value for the lattice energy favours the formation of an ionic lattice. Thus, a small metal atom (which will give a small cation) and high charges on both ions make the terms I and E unfavourable for the formation of a stable ionic bond, but at the same time they make the value of U more favourable. So it can be seen that only a very careful balancing of a number of different factors can lead to a correct prediction of whether a given compound will be ionic or not.

Factors which favour Covalent Bond Formation

Factors which will favour the formation of an ionic bond between two atoms have been considered at some length above. If a bond between two atoms is not ionic it is likely to be covalent (although intermetallic compounds and interstitial compounds are somewhat different), so that the factors which favour covalency are the opposite to those which favour ionic bond formation. Bonds are not necessarily purely ionic or purely covalent but are commonly intermediate in character. Consider again covalent and ionic bond formation to see how this can be so.

Suppose firstly that a covalent bond is formed between atoms A and B; each atom contributes one electron to the bond and these are shared between the two atoms. If A and B have the same electronegativity, both will attract the electron pair equally and the electrons can be considered to be as near to A as to B. If, however, B is more electronegative than A, it will attract the electron pair more strongly than will A; the limit of this process is that if there is a sufficiently large difference in electronegativity between the two atoms there is a complete transference of the pair of electrons from A to B. When this occurs, the net result is that B has gained one electron from A (besides regaining its own), and this is a pure ionic bond. Hence if there is a difference in the electronegativities of the two elements whose atoms form a covalent bond, the bond can be said to have some ionic character. When a bond is described as covalent it implies that it is predominantly covalent.

Alternatively, consider that an ionic bond is formed by the transference of one electron from atom A to atom B forming A^+B^-. The positively charged cation attracts not only the whole ion B^-, but more particularly the outermost electrons of the anion. If this attraction is particularly strong, it may be more correct to consider the electron and the one with which it has paired off as being shared by A and B. The separation of charges diminishes and the bond becomes covalent in character. This effect of distorting the electronic arrangement of the anion is known as polarisation; cations can be polarising and anions polarisable.

A cation which has a charge greater than unity will attract the electrons of the anion more strongly than one with unit charge, i.e. the polarising power of cations increases with the charge on the cation; similarly, an anion which has a charge greater than unity will tend to repel its outermost electrons more strongly than if it had unit charge, i.e. anions increase in polarisability with increase in the charge on the anion. The positive charge on a small cation has a stronger polarising effect on the electrons of the anion than a larger cation since it can approach more closely; similarly, the outermost electrons of a large anion are more easily polarisable than those of a smaller anion since they are further from the positive charge on the nucleus.

Fajans summarised the effect of polarisation by stating that a compound will tend to have appreciable covalent character if:

(i) either the anion or the cation is highly charged;
(ii) the cation is small;
(iii) the anion is large;
(iv) the cation does not have an inert gas type of electronic configuration.

The first three of these points have been considered above, but the fourth point requires further discussion. When the properties of compounds of the alkali metals are compared with those of the corresponding compounds of copper(I) and silver(I) it is seen that there is appreciable difference. For example, the alkali metal halides are water soluble, thermally stable and high melting, whereas the copper and silver halides are insoluble in water, decompose on heating and have much lower melting points; the alkali sulphides are very soluble in water and are colourless, whereas the sulphides of copper and silver are insoluble and deeply coloured. The sizes of the atoms (or ions) cannot account for the difference since they are similar—the silver ion is intermediate in size between the sodium and potassium ions, whereas the cuprous ion is slightly smaller than the sodium ion. The electronic configuration of the sodium and potassium ions is ns^2np^6, whereas those of copper(I) and silver(I) are $ns^2np^6(n-1)d^{10}$. It is considered that the d electrons screen the nuclear charge from the outermost electrons less efficiently than s and p electrons, so that ions behave as if they had a greater charge and hence show polarising properties; their compounds show properties associated with appreciable covalent character, and this is true of the transition metals as a whole when their ions do not have inert gas configurations.

The factors which influence bond type have now been discussed at some length. The importance of bond type will be seen when the structures of various compounds are described in later chapters.

Characteristic Features of Ionic and Covalent Compounds

Ionic and covalent compounds are different in character on account of the different nature of the bonds which hold them together. There is no sharp demarcation since compounds with bonds of intermediate character are intermediate in their properties also.

The most important difference between ionic and covalent compounds relates to structure. Bonds in covalent compounds have directional properties, and covalent molecules are usually discrete. In a crystal lattice these discrete molecules are arranged together in a convenient geometrical manner but are held together by the rather weak residual forces known as van der Waals' forces and hence do not approach each other very closely, i.e. not as closely as atoms of the same molecule, which are held together by a covalent bond. As a result of these weaker bonds many solid covalent compounds are more easily ruptured and so are soft and tend to have low melting and boiling points. There are however a number of covalent structures in which there are no discrete molecules and the covalent bonding is continuous throughout the crystal lattice, e.g. diamond (p. 129), silicon carbide (p. 75), silicon dioxide (p. 77), etc., and since there are no weaker van der Waals' forces in these structures they are usually hard and have high melting points.

In solid ionic compounds a positive ion attracts negative ions towards itself and they in turn attract further positive ions so that a lattice is built up of ions of positive and negative charge alternately which extends indefinitely in all directions and in which no discrete molecules, or indeed ion pairs, can be picked out. In contrast to covalent lattices there is no part of the structure weaker than any other, and hence the compounds are harder and have higher melting points and boiling points since strong electrostatic forces have to be overcome in breaking the structure in any way. (There are some lattices such as those of the cadmium halides, see p. 64, which are intermediate in bonding between ionic and covalent and which have some weak bonding and can be ruptured in certain directions preferentially.)

C

Decrease in melting point with increase in covalent character is illustrated by the following series, where the increase in covalent character follows the increase in the oxidation state of the electropositive element:

$$NaCl\ 800°;\ MgCl_2\ 712°;\ AlCl_3\ 193°*;\ SiCl_4\ -70°$$

When ionic compounds are fused, they conduct an electric current, and this current is carried by the ions of the compound and not by electrons which are responsible for the conduction in metals. Covalent compounds in contrast are non-conductors since they have neither free electrons nor ions to carry the current.

Another property which differentiates between ionic and covalent compounds is solubility. When an ionic compound is dissolved, the lattice is ruptured and the ions are held further apart in solution than in the solid state. There must be an interaction between the solvent and the ions which is more exoergic than the lattice energy since this latter is lost when the compound is dissolved. This interaction is the solvation energy and shows that the solvent molecules are attached to the ions in some way. The insolubility in water of the salts of the alkaline earth metals with polyvalent anions such as sulphate, oxalate and phosphate, etc., compared with the solubility of the corresponding alkali metal salts is attributed to their larger lattice energies. Solvents which have the power to solvate ions are those of high dielectric constant (p. 41), i.e. polar solvents, such as water, ammonia and hydrogen fluoride, etc. Solvents of low dielectric constant, i.e. non-polar solvents such as benzene, carbon tetrachloride, etc., do not solvate the ions and hence there is no solvation energy to offset the lattice energy, with the result that ionic compounds are not soluble in such solvents. In contrast, covalent compounds generally dissolve in non-polar but not in polar solvents. This behaviour is often summarised in the statement that like dissolves like.

Since a solution of an ionic compound in a polar solvent comprises solvated ions, the solution is able to conduct an electric current, and as in the fused solid, it is the ions which carry the current. There are some covalent molecules such as aluminium chloride which are changed into solvated ions on solution, and these solutions also conduct electricity.

The reactions of ionic compounds in solution are the reactions of their constituent ions, i.e. all ionic chlorides give the reactions characteristic of the chloride ion and of the appropriate cation, and these reactions occur instantaneously, e.g. precipitation reactions used in analysis. The reactions of covalent compounds in solution are characteristic of the whole molecule

* At 170 cm. pressure.

or of constituent functional groups and in general are not instantaneous, e.g. most organic reactions. Most covalent halides are hydrolysed by water whereas ionic halides are stable.

The contrast between the two types of compound is summarised in Table V.

TABLE V

Characteristic Properties of Ionic and Covalent Compounds

Ionic compounds	Covalent compounds
Crystal lattices are built of ions	Crystal lattices are built of molecules
Bonds are non-directional	Bonds are directional
Conductors when fused	Insulators when fused
Soluble in polar solvents	Insoluble in polar solvents
Insoluble in non-polar solvents	Soluble in non-polar solvents
High melting and boiling points	Low melting and boiling points
Reactions in solution are instantaneous	Reactions in solution take place at a measurable rate.

It should be emphasised that the properties in Table V are characteristic of ionic and covalent compounds on the whole, but there are exceptions, as have been pointed out in the previous pages. For example, quartz has a crystal lattice in which no discrete molecules can be detected, but when it is fused it does not conduct electricity; it has a very high melting point, but it is not soluble in polar solvents.

Atomic and Ionic Size

In preceding sections several references have been made to the relative sizes of atoms; it has also been seen that electrons do not travel at a fixed distance from the nucleus of an atom but that they can be found almost anywhere between the nucleus and infinity, although the most probable distance can often be calculated and is relatively near to the nucleus. Thus it is impossible to define precisely the extent of an isolated atom.

When atoms approach each other closely in the solid state they take up equilibrium positions in which the forces of attraction, e.g. chemical bonding, just balance the forces of repulsion, e.g. the repulsion of two positively charged nuclei. The sizes of the atoms must then be finite and so there is some significance in the term atomic radius. If radii can be assigned to atoms of all the elements, then it should be possible to predict interatomic distances, i.e. bond lengths, in compounds.

In practice, various physical techniques (see Chapter 2) can be used to determine the arrangements of atoms in space and the distances between atomic nuclei in solids. From these measurements atomic radii can be calculated and these radii can be used in their turn to calculate inter-atomic distances in other compounds. Radii calculated from physical measurements can be used in an additive way to predict other bond lengths only if they have been determined by measurements made on materials which show the same nature of bonding. To illustrate this, consider the C—Cl bond in methyl chloride; the C—C bond length in diamond is 1·54 Å (1 Å = 10^{-8} cm.), and since this represents the distance between the nuclei of two carbon atoms the atomic radius of carbon is $\frac{1}{2} \times 1·54 = 0·77$ Å; similarly, the Cl—Cl bond in the chlorine molecule is 1·98 Å, so that the atomic radius of chlorine is 0·99 Å. A C—Cl bond should therefore have a length of $0·99 + 0·77 = 1·76$ Å, and the value observed for the C—Cl bond in methyl chloride is $1·77 \pm 0·02$ Å. The agreement between calculated and observed is very good, showing that the principle of additivity is valid when, as is true of diamond, chlorine and methyl chloride, all the materials used in the measurements are covalently bonded. The radius of chlorine, or more correctly chloride, determined in ionic compounds is 1·81 Å, and if this had been used in the above calculation it would have given a very poor agreement.

Thus, two series may be compiled—atomic radii for use in covalent compounds and ionic radii for use in ionic compounds. The values for the atomic radii of metals are half the interatomic distances determined from measurements on pure metals, whereas those for non-metals are deter-mined in compounds which have a pure covalent bond, e.g. the N—N bond in hydrazine H_2N—NH_2. Atomic radii give incorrect values for bond length if the covalent bond is multiple, e.g. the C—C bond in ethylene is 1·33 Å compared with 1·54 Å in ethane, or if the bond has appreciable ionic character, i.e. if there is a large difference between the electronegativities of the two atoms.

The values of ionic radii are calculated from measurements made on ionic compounds. Although the distance between the nuclei of two oppositely charged ions is known, it is not obvious in what proportions the internuclear distance should be divided to give reasonable values for the two ionic radii. Semi-empirical methods have been used and these have produced self-consistent values. Normal ionic radii will give inaccurate values for interionic distances if the ionic bond has appreciable covalent character or if there is a change in the number of ions packed round a given ion. (It might be imagined that the apparent radius of the chloride ion would be different if there were six positively charged metal ions round it than if there were eight.) The degree of the inaccuracy can be assessed by studying the silver halides.

The silver ion is slightly polarising since it does not have an inert gas configuration (p. 24) and so the silver halides have some covalent character. This increases in the series AgF < AgCl < AgBr < AgI on account of the polarisability of the anions which increases in the same sequence. The ionic radii of the halide ions are determined from measurements of the alkali halides, which are ionic compounds, and the ionic radius of the silver ion is evaluated from the interionic distance in silver fluoride which is probably the most ionic silver compound. The interionic distances of the other silver halides are then calculated and are shown below compared with the observed values.

	AgF	AgCl	AgBr	AgI
Calculated	2·46	2·94	3·09	3·33
Observed	2·46	2·77	2·88	2·80
Percentage difference	—	6·1	7·2	18·9

The percentage difference is seen to increase with the increase in covalent character of the silver—halogen bond, the large increase in silver iodide being accounted for by the silver having only four nearest neighbours in silver iodide compared with six in the other silver halides.

A comparison of the ionic and atomic radii of sodium shows that the atomic radius is much larger. The sodium ion has the same number of protons in the nucleus as the sodium atom, but has one electron less; the nucleus of the ion can pull the smaller number of electrons closer to itself thereby producing a smaller value for its radius. Similarly, all cations are smaller than the neutral atoms from which they are derived. It follows also that when an element forms ions in different oxidation states (p. 6), the higher the oxidation state, i.e. the larger the number of electrons which have been removed from the neutral atom, the smaller will be the ionic radius. Similar reasoning makes it clear that an anion will have a larger radius than the neutral atom from which it is derived. In general, anions are larger than cations, although it is perhaps surprising to find that the fluoride ion is larger than the uranium(III) cation.

The atomic radius of the elements increases in a vertical group of the Periodic Table with increase in atomic number, i.e. with the number of shells of electrons which have to be accommodated round the nucleus. In successive elements the outermost electrons are occupying shells of ever-increasing principal quantum number. In horizontal periods there is no such increase in principal quantum number with increase in atomic number, and in contrast to the behaviour of the groups there is a gradual decrease in atomic radius along a period from left to right.

This horizontal decrease in atomic radius, when combined with the vertical increase, leads to a peculiar situation in the first and third long periods of the Table in which d and f levels respectively are filled for the first time. Thus scandium, the third element in the first long period, has the electronic configuration $4s^23d^1$, and not $4s^24p^1$ as might have been expected by analogy with the previous period. Aluminium has the electronic configuration $3s^23p^1$, and the next corresponding element to this is gallium of configuration $4s^23d^{10}4p^1$. Now calcium ($4s^2$) has a larger radius than magnesium ($3s^2$) and gallium would be expected to show a corresponding increase in size over aluminium, but because of the filling of the d level between scandium and gallium, there is a continuous decrease in atomic radius characteristic of all horizontal periods and so gallium is much smaller than if there were no filling of a d level, and is almost identical in radius to aluminium; i.e. the expected increase in atomic radius due to moving vertically from one period to the next is offset by the additional decrease in radius caused by moving ten additional units of atomic number in a horizontal direction. This effect can be called the d block contraction.

The corresponding f block, or as it is better known lanthanide, contraction is more profound in its effect since the element of greater atomic number, hafnium, has a smaller atomic radius than that of lower atomic number, zirconium. It might have been expected that the pairs of elements which have the same electronic configuration in their outermost shell and are now shown to have a very similar size, i.e. aluminium and gallium, zirconium and hafnium, and the corresponding pairs of elements which follow these in the Periodic Table would be very similar to each other in their chemical properties. This is more true of the pairs of elements which follow the f block contraction than of those which follow the d block contraction, and this can be attributed to different screening efficiency of d and f electrons.

Ionic radius shows the same trend as does atomic radius, but comparisons are more difficult in a horizontal period since it is not always possible to compare radii of successive elements in the same oxidation state due to the change in electronic configuration. In the d and f blocks $2+$ and $3+$ ions respectively are known for almost all the elements, and here the gradual tendency for the ions to decrease in size with increase in atomic-number is seen. The changes in radii are sufficiently small for a considerable number of isomorphous compounds to be formed in these series, most notably by the lanthanide elements.

2

METHODS USED FOR THE
DETERMINATION OF STRUCTURE

Introduction

In subsequent chapters the structures of a large number of compounds are described and in this chapter a brief account of the more important physical methods which are used to obtain structural information is given. More detailed descriptions of the methods are given elsewhere and it is intended to indicate here those properties of matter which can be studied to provide the necessary data.

Some methods can give precise values for the distances between atomic nuclei and for the angles between bonds, whereas other methods determine only the symmetry with which the atoms are arranged; for example, whether a triatomic molecule is linear or bent, or whether four bonds emanating from a central atom are directed to the corners of a tetrahedron or a square (see Fig. 7).

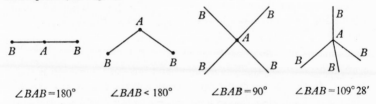

$\angle BAB = 180°$ $\angle BAB < 180°$ $\angle BAB = 90°$ $\angle BAB = 109°28'$

Fig. 7 Possible symmetries of molecules AB_2 and AB_4.

The methods vary in the ease with which they can be applied, so that, for example, a dipole moment can be obtained much more quickly than an X-ray crystallographic study can be completed. The various methods will be discussed under the following headings:

   (i) Spectra.

  (ii) Diffraction.

 (iii) Magnetic measurements.

 (iv) Dipole moments.

Spectra

It was seen in Chapter 1 that atoms have different electronic energy levels and that these can be said to be quantised in that their number is determined by certain quantum numbers and is finite, although very large. It was also seen that when an atom gains a sufficient amount of energy an electron is promoted to a higher energy level, and this same amount of energy is given out when the electron falls back to its original level or ground state.

Molecules also have electronic energy levels, and in addition have vibrational and rotational energy levels. That is to say, there are different modes in which the molecules can vibrate and rotate according to the amount of energy which they possess, and these energy levels are also quantised. The differences in energy between successive electronic levels are much greater than those between successive vibrational levels and still greater than those between successive rotational levels. Rotational energies are so low that molecules are only in their lowest level or ground state near the absolute zero of temperature. At room temperature the thermal energy acquired by being three hundred degrees above the absolute zero promotes the molecules to higher levels.

When a molecule is exposed to radiation of a suitable wavelength, i.e. of suitable energy, transitions from one energy level to another take place. For electronic transitions, which require the largest amount of energy of the three types of transition being considered, radiation of very short wavelength is required* corresponding to the ultra-violet (u.v.) region of the spectrum; for vibrational transitions, radiation of lower energy and hence of higher wavelength is required and this corresponds to the near infra-red (i.r.) region; finally, for rotational transitions the required radiation is of still lower energy and higher wavelength which corresponds to the far infra-red region.

Molecular spectra are usually studied by irradiating the appropriate substance and scanning the transmitted radiation. As a result of the passage of radiation through a substance the intensities of certain wavelengths of the radiation decrease; the absorption of radiation of a particular wavelength brings about transitions in the molecules because the energy of the radiation corresponds to the energy of the appropriate transition. A knowledge of the wavelength of the absorbed radiation thus

---

* $E = hc/\lambda$, where E (ergs) is the energy associated with the radiation, λ (cm.) is its wavelength, and c (cm. sec.$^{-1}$) is its velocity, and h is Planck's constant and has the value of $6 \cdot 62 \times 10^{-27}$ (erg sec.); i.e. energy is inversely proportional to the wavelength of the radiation.

gives the energy of a molecular transition, and this can be related to information about the structure of the molecule.

To illustrate this, consider the simple case of a diatomic molecule AB which has a permanent dipole moment (p. 41). The moment of inertia, I, of the molecule is given by the equation

$$I = Mr^2,$$

where r is the internuclear distance and M is the reduced mass of the molecule. (M is defined by the equation $\dfrac{1}{M} = \dfrac{1}{m_A} + \dfrac{1}{m_B}$, where m_A and m_B are the masses of A and B respectively.) The pure rotational spectrum of such a molecule consists of a number of equally spaced lines and the difference in wavelength between two adjacent lines, i.e. corresponding to successive energy levels, can be measured; then, it can be shown that

$$\Delta\lambda = \frac{4\pi^2 Ic}{hJ} = \frac{4\pi^2 Mr^2 c}{hJ},$$

where J is a quantum number.

Since r the internuclear distance is the only unknown quantity in this equation, it can be calculated, and this is the bond length.

The rotational spectra of larger molecules and both vibrational and electronic spectra are more difficult to interpret.

A somewhat different technique is used to study Raman spectra. When a substance is irradiated, most of the radiation passes straight through, and the above methods of absorption spectra utilised this property. However, a small proportion of the radiation is scattered and some of this can be detected in a direction at right angles to the incident beam. When the incident beam is monochromatic, i.e. of one wavelength only, the scattered radiation has lines of more than one wavelength, and this is the Raman spectrum. The radiation which is scattered gives up some of its energy to bring about a transition in the molecule, and since it must then have a lower energy than originally, it follows that it has a longer wavelength; the difference in wavelength corresponds to the energy of the transition that has been brought about in the molecule. Less frequently some of the radiation strikes a molecule which is in an excited state; the molecule falls back to a lower energy level, giving the excess of energy to the scattered radiation which then has a lower wavelength than the incident radiation. Thus the Raman spectrum comprises a line of the same wavelength as the incident radiation with a number of lines of higher and lower wavelengths. The information which can be obtained is similar to that obtained from absorption spectra, and is often complementary.

Diffraction

When a beam of light strikes a series of fine lines ruled on the surface of a glass plate at a spacing corresponding approximately to the wavelength of the light, each line acts as a centre from which a secondary train of light waves spreads out. This is known as diffraction. In some directions the diffracted beams interfere with each other and cancel out, whereas in other directions they reinforce each other.

It was suggested by von Laue in 1912 that if crystals were built of atoms arranged in a lattice at distances apart which were of the same order of magnitude as the wavelength of X-rays, a crystal lattice should act as a diffraction grating for X-rays; diffraction patterns should thus be produced by the passage of an X-ray beam through matter and these should be characteristic of the arrangements of atoms in the substance irradiated and of the wavelength of the particular X-radiation used. These suggestions were proved to be correct and the diffraction of X-rays by crystals has become the most powerful method for the determination of the structures of compounds.

Each crystal lattice is built up by infinite repetition of a small unit, just as is a wallpaper pattern. Whereas the wallpaper is two-dimensional, the crystal is three-dimensional; this unit is known as the 'unit cell' and is defined by quoting the lengths of the three axes and the interaxial angles, which are often, but by no means always, 90°. The length of an axis is thus the least distance travelled in that particular direction before the pattern repeats itself.

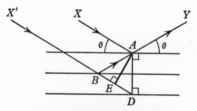

Fig. 8 The reflection of X-rays by
parallel planes.

A crystal can be thought of as comprising a series of hypothetical planes, some of which contain atoms whereas others do not, and since the pattern of the crystal is repeating, there are series of parallel planes; the X-ray beam is reflected by these planes. Consider a series of parallel planes through a crystal as shown in Fig. 8. XA and $X'B$ represent two incident X-rays which impinge upon consecutive planes and are reflected along the same path AY; the angle of incidence, and hence the angle of reflection, is θ. The two X-rays will reinforce each other if after reflection they are coincident, i.e. the crest of a wave of the one coincides with a crest of the other and a trough coincides with a trough. If the waves are not coincident, they cancel out. For coincidence to occur, the distances travelled by the two rays must differ by an integral number of wavelengths; this difference in distance is referred to as the path difference. An inspection of Fig. 8 shows that the path difference is $AB-BE$.

Now, $\angle BAD = \angle ADB = 90° - \theta$

hence $AB = BD.$

Thus the path difference between the two rays is given by,

$$AB - BE = BD - BE = ED = AD \sin \theta.$$

Also, $AD = 2d$, where d is the perpendicular distance between two adjacent planes; the condition that the rays should reinforce each other, i.e. that the path difference must equal an integral number of wavelengths, is thus given by the relationship

$$n\lambda = AD \sin \theta,$$

or $$n\lambda = 2d \sin \theta,$$

where λ is the wavelength of the X-rays and n is an integer. In any experiment, λ is known and θ can be found for different values of n, so that the spacing between the planes in the crystal can be evaluated.

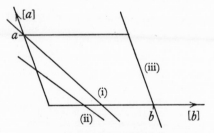

Fig. 9 Derivation of Miller indices.

Although an infinite number of planes can be drawn through a crystal, the number which can reflect the X-ray beam is finite. To amplify this statement, consider the system used in naming the various planes. In Fig. 9 are shown the [a] and [b] axes of a crystal with unit axial lengths a and b marked off; the third axis [c] is at right angles to the plane of the paper. The three lines (i), (ii) and (iii) represent planes parallel to the [c] axis and hence intersecting it at infinity. The intercepts on the three axes can then be written as

	a	b	c
(i)	1	$\frac{1}{2}$	∞
(ii)	$\frac{1}{2}$	$\frac{1}{3}$	∞
(iii)	∞	1	∞

If these values of the intercepts are taken in the order [a], [b] and [c] and are then inverted, the indices of the three planes become respectively (i) 1 2 0, (ii) 2 3 0 and (iii) 0 1 0. These are known as the Miller indices of the appropriate planes. The planes which are able to reflect the X-ray beam usually have small values for their Miller indices.

When a crystal is rotated in an X-ray beam about one of its axes, each set of planes which has zero as the Miller index for the axis of rotation becomes orientated in turn in such a position that the condition $n\lambda = 2d$ sin θ applies and the X-ray beam is reflected at the angle θ, which is a characteristic of the particular set of planes. The diffracted beams produce a pattern of spots on a photographic film, one spot corresponding to each set of planes, and the pattern which is obtained depends upon the geometry of the unit cell. The various spots vary considerably in their relative intensities and these relative intensities are measured visually to provide the experimental data required for a structure determination. The intensities of the reflections are dependent upon the positions of the atoms within the unit cell. (Further photographs can be taken to give a more complete record, i.e. rotations about the other two axes.)

Perhaps the most commonly used method of structure determination is that known as the trial-and-error method; in this an approximate set of positions for the atoms within the unit cell is first guessed by using various pieces of evidence and not least chemical intuition; it is possible to calculate the contributions of all the atoms in the unit cell to each observed reflection and thus to obtain theoretical values for the intensities of all the spots on the photographic film based on this trial structure; these are then compared with the observed values. If agreement is poor the trial structure is probably incorrect, but if agreement is good the atomic positions are adjusted until the best possible agreement is obtained between the theoretical and the observed intensities. The process involves long mathematical computation, but at the end can produce very accurate atomic positions, thus giving both bond lengths and bond angles and not merely molecular symmetry.

The diffraction of electrons and neutrons have both been used for determination of structures, although their use is not as extensive as the use of X-rays. Electrons have a lower penetrating power than X-rays and for this reason electron diffraction is usually applied to gaseous materials. The method has its limitations and is most satisfactory with small molecules. Neutron diffraction is very similar to X-ray diffraction in many ways and is used to investigate the structure of single crystals. Neutron sources are not as readily available as X-ray sources since the most convenient generation of neutrons requires atomic fission, e.g. an atomic pile; neutrons are not detected by a photographic film and the counting techniques required are more tedious; the intensity of a neutron beam is lower than that of an X-ray beam and so considerably longer exposures are required.

Perhaps the most important difference, however, is that X-rays are scattered primarily by electrons whereas neutrons are scattered by atomic nuclei. As a consequence the various isotopes of the same element differ from each other in their power to scatter neutrons although they have the same power to scatter X-rays since the number of electrons remains the same in different isotopes of the same element. The main advantage of neutron diffraction compared with X-ray diffraction lies in the greater ease with which light atoms can be detected, especially in molecules which contain heavier atoms also. The scattering of an X-ray beam by an atom is proportional to its atomic number, and so a uranium atom scatters X-rays ninety-two times more strongly than does a hydrogen atom. This makes it extremely difficult to resolve the position of light atoms at all accurately since their contributions to the various reflections are swamped by those of heavier atoms which are also present; hydrogen atoms are difficult to detect even in organic molecules which contain no elements heavier than carbon and oxygen. The factor between the extremes of scattering power in the case of neutrons is only three and so the light atoms and especially hydrogen can be detected much more easily by neutron diffraction than by X-ray diffraction.

Magnetic Measurements

When a material is less permeable to magnetic lines of force than is a vacuum, it tends to move from a stronger to a weaker part of an inhomogeneous magnetic field and is said to be diamagnetic. When a material is more permeable and moves from a weaker to a stronger part of the field it is said to be paramagnetic.

The molar paramagnetic susceptibility of a compound is the intensity of magnetisation induced in a g.mol. of a compound by unit applied magnetic field,* and is given by the equation:

$$\chi = \frac{N\mu^2}{3kT},\tag{1}$$

where N is Avogadro's number
μ is the magnetic moment of the compound
k is a known constant (Boltzmann)
T is the absolute temperature.

Experimentally χ can be determined, for example, by means of a Gouy balance. The substance whose paramagnetic susceptibility is required is placed in a tube of cross-section a which is suspended in a balance and a strong magnetic field H is applied across one end, the field strength at the other end being small enough to be neglected. Then the apparent mass of the substance is determined with and without the application of the magnetic field. If the difference in apparent mass is Δm, then the force F acting on the substance is given by

$$F = \Delta m \cdot g,\tag{2}$$

where g is the acceleration due to gravity. It can also be shown that

$$F = \tfrac{1}{2}(K_1 - K_2) \cdot H^2 \cdot a,\tag{3}$$

where K_1 is the volume susceptibility of the material and K_2 is the volume susceptibility of air.

Combining (2) and (3),

$$\Delta m \cdot g = \tfrac{1}{2}(K_1 - K_2) \cdot H^2 \cdot a,$$

thus
$$K_1 = K_2 + \frac{2\Delta m \cdot g}{aH^2}.$$

K_2 is a known quantity and the required quantity χ is given by

$$\chi = \frac{K_1 M}{\rho} = \frac{M}{\rho}\left(K_2 + \frac{2\Delta m \cdot g}{aH^2}\right),$$

where M and ρ are the molecular weight and the density of the substance respectively. It is usually the value of μ, the magnetic moment of the molecule, which is quoted and from (1) it can be seen that

$$\mu = \sqrt{3kT\chi/N}.$$

* A substance which is paramagnetic also shows diamagnetism, but this is much weaker and is neglected in this discussion.

Those compounds in which all the electrons are paired (see Chapter 1) are diamagnetic, but compounds which possess unpaired electrons are paramagnetic and the value of the magnetic moment indicates the number of unpaired electrons. This experimentally obtained knowledge frequently affords information as to the structure of the compound and this will be referred to in Chapter 6 (p. 113).

A more recent technique is the study of nuclear magnetic resonance (N.M.R.). The magnetic measurements discussed above depend upon the spin of unpaired electrons, whereas N.M.R. measures magnetic effects caused by the spin of protons and neutrons (known collectively as nucleons). A large number of atomic species (nuclides) comprise an even number of protons and an even number of neutrons, i.e. even atomic number and even mass number, and these do not have any nuclear magnetism, which is a limitation of the method. Since no isotope of hydrogen is an 'even-even' nuclide, N.M.R. is able to yield information about the position of hydrogen atoms, and the importance of this lies in the difficulty of finding them by X-ray crystallographic methods as referred to above. Nuclear magnetic susceptibilities are smaller in magnitude than electronic magnetic susceptibilities by a factor of 10^6 and the technique of their measurement is consequently much more difficult.

The number of possible orientations which a nuclear magnet can assume is quantised (cf. electronic levels) and the difference in the energy level of these different orientations is very small. The frequency of the radiation associated with transitions from one state to another can be calculated and is given by

$$v = \frac{gHe}{4M_pc},$$

where M_p is the mass of a proton
   H is the strength of the external magnetic field
   g is an empirical constant and differs for each nuclide
   e is the charge on an electron
   c is the velocity of light.

This frequency is known as the Larmor frequency.

Consider a simple case where only two different orientations are possible. The energy levels of the two orientations are close together, and at equilibrium only a slight excess of nuclei are in the one orientation compared with the number in the other. If the magnetic properties of this nuclide are studied by irradiation, only the very few nuclei can absorb radiation and change their energy state, so that the change in radiation intensity is very small indeed. However, if the radiation used is of the Larmor frequency, a resonance effect is set up which magnifies the effect considerably. This resonance can be compared with the well-known phenomenon of a bridge being caused to vibrate when struck repeatedly by a relatively weak force which acts at the natural frequency of the bridge.

The value of g for a particular nuclide must be determined experimentally using a known compound, and since there are no other unknowns in the above equation, the Larmor frequency can be calculated for any appropriate field strength; the Larmor frequency is directly proportional to the field strength.

If a substance is irradiated with radiation of the Larmor frequency calculated for a particular type of nuclide present in its molecule, absorption of the radiation occurs. If the field strength is then varied, so too is the Larmor frequency, and so the incident radiation is no longer of the critical frequency and absorption decreases sharply. If the absorption of the radiation is plotted against a change in field strength, ΔH (and hence against a change in the Larmor frequency $\Delta \nu$), then for a species, i.e. molecule or ion, which contains a single atom of the nuclide whose resonance is being studied, a plot is obtained as shown in Fig. 10a; but if the species contains more than one atom of that nuclide these interact with each other and produce an absorption curve of a different shape; that obtained for two atoms is shown in Fig. 10b.

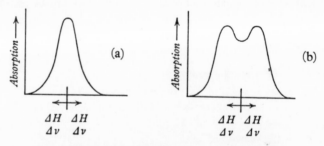

FIG. 10 Absorption curves for a single nucleus and for a pair of nuclei.

A good illustration of this approach is the work of Deeley and Richards on the so-called infusible white precipitate. Structures had been proposed for this compound incorporating variously NH_4^+ ions, NH_3 molecules and NH_2 groups. The shape of the absorption curve for the hydrogen spectrum unambiguously indicated that there were two hydrogens interacting with one another, and so the first two of the above suggestions are ruled out. The compound is formulated $HgNH_2Cl$.

Whereas the shape of the absorption curve gives an indication of the number of nuclei of a given type which are present, the separation of the absorption maxima depends upon the distance apart of the particular nuclei and so it is possible to evaluate interatomic distances by this method. Note that this is not necessarily the same as 'bond length'; an N.M.R. study of the ammonium ion would yield the distance between pairs of hydrogen atoms, but a value of the N—H bond length can be evaluated only if the bond angle H—N—H is also known, i.e. from the symmetry, which in this case is tetrahedral, so that the angle is 109° 28'.

Dipole Moments

When a covalent bond is formed between two atoms of unequal electro-negativity, it follows that the electrons are unequally shared between the two atoms. This can be considered as a small positive charge δ on the less electronegative atom and a small negative charge on the other atom. This is known as an electric dipole, and if the atoms are at a distance d apart the dipole moment μ is given by $\mu = \delta d$, and it acts along the direction of the bond. When there are a number of dipoles in a molecule, the resultant moment in any direction is obtained by the addition of the vectors of the individual moments in that direction.

When a compound which is an insulator (a property of covalent compounds) is placed between the plates of a capacitor (condenser), the capacitance (capacity) is increased by a factor ϵ which is known as the dielectric constant of the compound, i.e. $\epsilon = c/c_0$ where c_0 is the capacitance of the capacitor in a vacuum and c is the capacitance when the insulator is between the plates. An increase in the capacitance results in a decrease in the strength of the electric field. This effect is caused not only by any permanent dipole moment which exists in a molecule of the insulator but also by a temporary dipole moment which is induced in all molecules by an electric field. This induced dipole moment is a slight separation of charges under the influence of the field, which reverts to normal as soon as the field is switched off.

The capacitance is measured at different temperatures, and values for the dielectric constant ϵ of the insulator are obtained. Then it can be shown that for gases or dilute solutions of polar materials in non-polar solvents,

$$\left(\frac{\epsilon-1}{\epsilon+2}\right)\frac{M}{\rho}=\frac{4\pi N}{3}\left(\alpha_D+\frac{\mu^2}{3kT}\right),$$

D

where M is the molecular weight of the insulator

ρ is the density of the insulator

μ is the Avogadro number

N is the dipole moment

k is the Boltzmann constant

T is the absolute temperature

a_D is the contribution of the induced dipole moment.

Let the left-hand side of the equation equal y; then the equation can be seen to be of the form $y = A + B(1/T)$. Hence if y is plotted against $1/T$, the gradient of the line B can be measured and can be seen to be $4\pi N\mu^2/9k$. Since μ the dipole moment of the insulator is the only unknown in this equation, it can be calculated.

The measurement of dipole moments is particularly useful in determining whether a certain molecule has a centrosymmetric structure or not. A centrosymmetric structure can have no dipole moment as the moments of the individual bonds cancel out when the vectors are added. This can be illustrated by considering molecules of type XY_2. If the three atoms are linear, the molecule is centrosymmetric and has no dipole moment, e.g. CO_2; if, however, the three atoms are not linear, the molecule does not have a centre of symmetry and hence has a dipole moment, e.g. SO_2. Although molecules of type XY_3 cannot be centrosymmetric, if the three atoms of Y form an equilateral triangle round the central atom of X so that all four atoms are coplanar, the vectors of the X—Y bond moments cancel out and the molecule has no overall dipole moment, e.g. BF_3. If however the atom of X is not coplanar with the atoms of Y, the structure is pyramidal and the vectors of the X—Y bond moments do not cancel out so that the molecule does have an overall resultant dipole moment, eg NF_3.

It is often possible to differentiate between pairs of geometrical isomers bv dipole moment measurements. For example, consider the compound dichloro diammino platinum(II). This is known to exist in two isomeric forms, which are as shown in Fig. 11, the four bonds emanating from the platinum atom being directed to the corners of a square plane.

FIG. 11 *trans-* and *cis-*dichloro diammino platinum(II).

The moments of the Pt—Cl bond cancel out when the bonds Cl—Pt—Cl are collinear (i.e. the three atoms have a centre of symmetry), and similarly the moments of the Pt—N bond. Thus in structure (i), known as the trans isomer, the bond moments cancel out and the molecule has no permanent dipole moment. No such cancellation of moments can occur in structure (ii), known as the cis isomer, which thus has a permanent dipole moment. The existence of the two isomers, which have different properties, is evidence also for the planar structure since no such isomerism is possible if the four bonds from the central atom are arranged tetrahedrally.

Such an argument as the above is typical of those used in classical stereochemistry which provided evidence for the tetrahedral arrangement of bonds from carbon atoms. The existence of optical isomerism in carbon compounds which possess asymmetric centres and whose molecules are not superimposable upon their mirror images need not be considered here, but this approach has been used to show that elements other than carbon have tetrahedral arrangements of bonds. As an example, the complex formed by zinc with benzoyl pyruvic acid, which is shown below, can be seen to have no plane or centre of symmetry, and so cannot be superimposed upon its mirror image, if the arrangement of the four bonds from the central zinc atom is tetrahedral. The resolution of the compound into two optically active isomers proves that this is so.

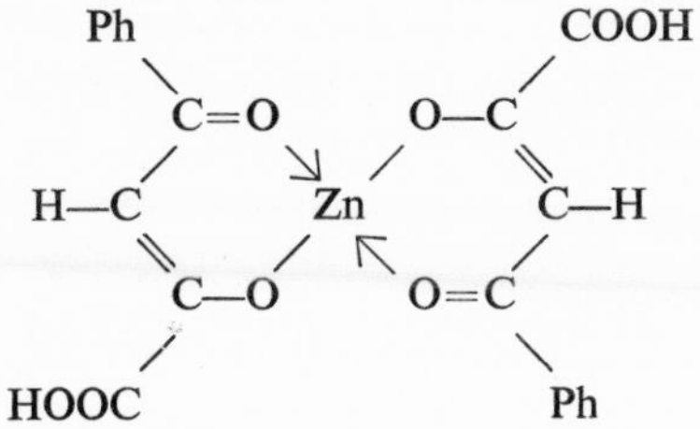

3

THE STRUCTURES OF THE METALLIC ELEMENTS AND OF CERTAIN COMPOUNDS WITH THREE-DIMENSIONAL LATTICES

The Close-packing of Spheres

If a number of spheres of equal size is put in a box and shaken, they will arrange themselves in such a way as to occupy the minimum volume of space. In order to see what this arrangement is, consider first how spheres can be arranged in one plane. It is obvious that the arrangement in Fig. 12*b* is more closely packed than that in Fig. 12*a* and is indeed the most economical arrangement possible. It can be calculated that in the arrangement shown in Fig. 12*b* 60·4 per cent. of the available space is filled with spheres whereas in that shown in Fig. 12*a* only 52·4 per cent. of the space is filled. Any sphere in the close-packed layer is in contact with six others which make a hexagonal pattern around it, i.e. it has six nearest neighbours. The number of nearest neighbours is called the *coordination number*.

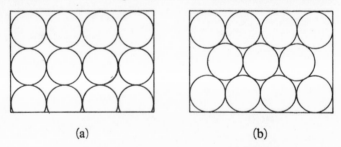

(a)   (b)

FIG. 12 Close-packing of spheres in two dimensions.

Consider next how successive layers will build up on top of the first layer. Imagine Fig. 12 to be an elevation instead of a plan and it is apparent that Fig. 12*b* is again the more economical. This means that a sphere in the second layer fits into a hollow at the centre of three touching spheres in the first layer, when the centres of these four spheres will be at the corners of a regular tetrahedron, as shown in Fig. 13. The remaining spheres in the second layer then fit in other hollows in the first layer, and the second layer also has a close-packed pattern as shown in plan in

Fig. 14. Spheres in one layer are shown in solid lines and those in the other layer in broken lines. The centres of the spheres in the second layer are marked by dots and it can be seen that there is an equal number of unfilled hollows on top of the first layer, and these are marked '*x*' in the Figure.

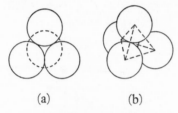

(a)   (b)

FIG. 13 The formation of a tetrahedral
site by close-packed spheres.

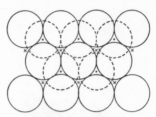

FIG. 14 Two layers of close-
packed spheres.

There are two alternative ways in which the third layer can pack on top of the second layer. The third layer can lie vertically above the first, which it can do by resting in one set of hollows on top of the second layer, or, alternatively, it can lie in the other set of hollows on top of the second layer which correspond to those marked '*x*' in the first layer and lie directly above them. The first alternative can be represented as *ABA* and the second as *ABC*, where the letters denote the different orientations of the respective layers.

When the first arrangement of layers is continued indefinitely in the sequence *ABABABABA*, etc., it possesses what is known as hexagonal symmetry. (Note carefully point (1) on p. 47 in connection with this terminology.) This means that the whole structure has a six-fold axis of symmetry* which is perpendicular to the planes of close-packed spheres. Because of its symmetry this arrangement of spheres is called *hexagonal close-packing*, and it is illustrated in Fig. 15.

When the second arrangement of layers is continued indefinitely in the sequence *ABCABCABCABCA*, etc., it possesses not hexagonal but cubic symmetry, which means that the whole structure has four three-fold axes of symmetry,* and this arrangement of spheres is called *cubic close-packing*. It is useful at this stage to describe this cubic symmetry in greater detail. The four three-fold axes of a cube are the body diagonals of the cube, i.e. they traverse the cube from one corner to the diametrically opposite corner. It was noted that the symmetry axis in the hexagonal close-packed

* An *n*-fold axis of symmetry is such that when a structure is rotated about that axis the same arrangement of the structure recurs *n* times in the course of a complete revolution.

arrangement is perpendicular to the layers of close-packed spheres. This is true in the cubic system also, but there are four three-fold axes. In consequence, if layers of spheres are built up in the sequence *ABCABCABCA*, etc., in a given direction, exactly similar sequences of close-packed layers will be found in three other directions also, the four directions intersecting each other at the same angle as the body diagonals of a cube intersect each other. This illustrates the high symmetry of the cubic system.

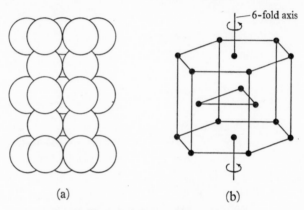

Fig. 15 Hexagonal close-packing arrangement.

When a model of cubic close-packed spheres is studied it becomes apparent that there is a sphere at the centre of each face of the unit cube and accordingly this arrangement of spheres is also known as face-centred cubic. In a number of the Figures which illustrate various structures later in this chapter it is easy to see that atoms of one kind are arranged in a face-centred cubic lattice, and it should be remembered that this is the arrangement of cubic close-packing even although the close-packed layers are not easily detectable. A face-centred cube is shown in Fig. 16*a*; in Fig. 16*b* the cube has been redrawn with one of its body diagonals vertical (such a diagonal is a three-fold axis); it can be seen that the corners and face centres of the cube lie in planes which are perpendicular to the cube diagonal and in these planes can be seen the pattern associated with a close-packed layer, i.e. layers of close-packing are perpendicular to the symmetry axis. Successive layers are shown with different symbols to illustrate the *ABCA* arrangement of the layers required for cubic close-packing.

There are several points concerning close-packing which should be emphasised:

(1) The hexagonal pattern of spheres around a given sphere in a close-packed layer is not to be confused with the overall symmetry; the hexagonal pattern is found in all layers in both types of close-packing whereas the overall symmetry is determined by the sequence of the close-packed layers and is hexagonal only if that sequence is *ABABABA*, etc.

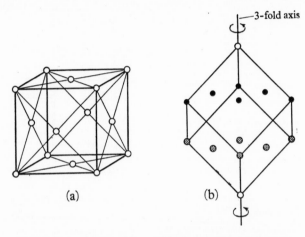

FIG. 16 Face-centred cubic, or cubic close-packing arrangement.

(2) In addition to being in contact with six nearest neighbours in one layer, a given sphere is in contact with three spheres in the layer above and three in the layer below, so that it has twelve nearest neighbours, i.e. a coordination number of twelve.

(3) An irregular arrangement of layers such as *ABABABCABABC*, etc., possesses neither cubic nor hexagonal symmetry but a lower symmetry.

(4) In either type of close-packing 74·0 per cent. of the available space is occupied by the spheres.

The Structures of the Metallic Elements

Apart from a few exceptions such as manganese, uranium, etc. (which will not be considered), most metals in the *s* and *d* blocks of the Periodic Table have their atoms arranged according to one or more (i.e. polymorphic) of three simple types of structure:

(i) cubic close-packing
(ii) hexagonal close-packing
(iii) body-centred cubic.

The first two of these arrangements have been described in detail above. A body-centred cubic arrangement has an atom at each corner and also at the centre of the unit cube, and is illustrated in Fig. 17. (It is called

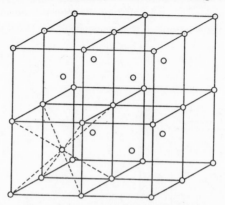

FIG. 17 Body-centred cubic arrangement.

body-centred to differentiate it from face-centred.) Each atom in a body-centred arrangement has eight nearest neighbours disposed towards the corners of a cube with six other atoms (which correspond to the centres of adjacent cubes) only slightly further distant. The body-centred cubic arrangement cannot be regarded as being close-packed since close-packing requires a coordination number of twelve. Whereas the close-packing of spheres fills 74 per cent. of available space, a body-centred cubic arrangement fills 68 per cent., so that it is nearly as economical as close-packing.

Li	Be										
c	b										
Na	Mg										
c	b										
K	Ca	Sc	Ti	V	Cr	Mn	Fe	Co	Ni	Cu	Zn
c	a,b	a,b	b,c	c	c	—	a,c	a,b	a,b	a	b
Rb	Sr	Y	Zr	Nb	Mo	Tc	Ru	Rh	Pd	Ag	Cd
c	a	b	b,c	c	b,c	b	a,b	a	a	a	b
Cs	Ba	La	Hf	Ta	W	Re	Os	Ir	Pt	Au	Hg
c	c	a,b	b,c	c	c	b	a,b	a	a	a	—

a=cubic close-packed   b=hexagonal close-packed
c=body-centred cubic

FIG. 18. The structures of the metallic elements.

Thus it is seen that the structures of most metals are either close-packed or nearly so, and also that they are of high symmetry; the lower symmetry expected from an order of layers such as *ABABABCABABC*, etc., being unknown or rare in metal structures. Economy of packing and high symmetry will be found in the structures of many simple compounds also.

The structures found for *s* and *d* block metals are indicated in Fig. 18; the inert gases also have close-packed structures. The structures of the remaining metals and the non-metals will be considered in Chapter 7.

Interstitial Sites in Close-packed Lattices

It was pointed out above (p. 45, Fig. 13) that when one sphere rests upon three other touching spheres a tetrahedral arrangement is produced. Since spheres touch each other at one point only there must be a space at the centre of this tetrahedron which can be called a *tetrahedral site*. This does not mean that the shape of the site is tetrahedral but that the centres of the four surrounding spheres are disposed towards the corners of a regular tetrahedron. The size of a tetrahedral site is very much smaller than the size of the surrounding spheres, although the larger are the spheres the larger the site will be. In a close-packed lattice each sphere is in contact with three spheres in the layer above and three in the layer below so that there are two tetrahedral sites associated with each sphere, one immediately above it and the other immediately below it, irrespective of whether the close-packing be cubic or hexagonal.

There is a second type of interstitial site in close-packed lattices. This is situated at the centre of an arrangement of six spheres the centres of which form a regular octahedron, and which is therefore called an *octahedral site*. (The prefix octa- means eight and an octahedron has eight sides and eight faces but only six corners.) An octahedron standing on one corner is illustrated in Fig. 19*a* and an octahedron lying on one face is illustrated in Fig. 19*b*. The former arrangement represents the octahedron

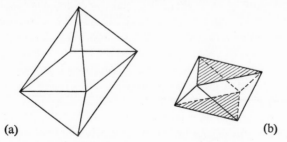

(a)   (b)

FIG. 19 Two different orientations of an octahedron.

as a square equatorial plane with apices above and below, whereas the latter arrangement, which is easier to pick out in a close-packed lattice, can be described as comprising two equilateral triangles in parallel planes with their apices pointing in opposite directions. Now consider the two layers of close-packed spheres shown in plan in Fig. 20; triangles are drawn each of which joins the centres of three spheres in one plane, and octahedral sites, marked 'x', are found where two triangles in different layers are superimposed one above the other and have their apices pointing in opposite directions.

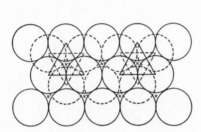

FIG. 20 The formation of octahedral sites by close-packed spheres.

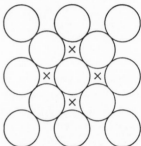

FIG. 21 The 100 face of a face-centred cube, showing the cross-section of octahedral sites.

In considering the building up of successive layers of close-packed spheres (p. 45), it was seen that a second layer rests in a set of hollows on top of the first layer, and that there is an equivalent set of hollows on which the spheres of the second layer do not rest. The first set of hollows are now seen to be tetrahedral sites whereas the second set are the octahedral sites.

In Fig. 21 is shown the face of a face-centred cubic (i.e. cubic close-packed) lattice and the positions marked 'x' are the centres of equatorial planes of octahedral sites. It is useful to remember the two alternative ways of regarding an octahedron so that octahedral sites can be easily recognised in various structures. It can be seen by a consideration of Fig. 19 that there is one octahedral site associated with each sphere in a close-packed lattice, i.e. only half the number of tetrahedral sites.

An octahedral site is larger than a tetrahedral site, and again varies in size with the size of the surrounding spheres. The size of the site relative to the size of the spheres can be determined by simple trigonometry. A cross-section through an octahedral site is shown in Fig. 22 (cf. Fig. 21); let a small sphere fit into the site so that it just touches the four larger spheres; let A be the centre of the smaller sphere and B and C the centres of two of the larger spheres. It is then obvious from the geometry of the figure that BC passes through the point of contact of the two spheres at point D and that AD is perpendicular to BC. Then $BD=AD=r_2=$the radius of the larger sphere. Let r_1 be the radius of the smaller sphere. Then since triangle ABD is right-angled, by Pythagoras,

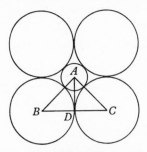

FIG. 22 A cross-section through an octahedral site.

$$AB^2=AD^2+BD^2,$$

i.e. $$(r_1+r_2)^2=r_2^2+r_2^2=2r_2^2$$

Hence $$r_1+r_2=\sqrt{2}r_2=1\cdot414 \cdot r_2$$

i.e. $$r_1=0\cdot414 \cdot r_2$$

or $$r_1/r_2=0\cdot414.$$

Thus the smaller sphere must be rather less than half the size of the larger spheres which surround it. It can also be shown that for a tetrahedral site $r_1/r_2=0\cdot225$, so that a tetrahedral site is significantly smaller than an octahedral site.

Consider again the structure of pure metals; in a single crystal, deformation should be possible by causing one plane of atoms to slide over another. This should be easier in the cubic system than in the hexagonal system since there are more directions in which sliding is possible, i.e. in planes parallel to the layers of close-packing. It was seen earlier that a cubic crystal has four three-fold axes of symmetry and a hexagonal crystal only one six-fold axis and that layers of close-packed atoms are found at right angles to these axes (p. 45). Hence cubic metals should be more easily deformed, i.e. more malleable and more ductile, than hexagonal metals.

With this picture of the structure of metals it is easy to see how the introduction of some larger metal atoms into the lattice to make an alloy will make the metal more difficult to deform since the sliding of layers over each other will be rendered more difficult. Similarly the presence of a small number of very small atoms such as the non-metals carbon or nitrogen which can fit into the interstitial sites will change the physical properties of the metal in the same way, e.g. carbon in steel; in this case any chemical bonding between the metal and the non-metal atoms will increase the resistance to deformation.

The Structures of Some Simple Compounds

In the previous section it was seen that the structures of many metallic elements involve an arrangement whereby atoms are packed as economically as possible in space. It might be expected that a similar economy of space would be achieved in the structures of compounds also, and a consideration of the structures of very many simple inorganic compounds shows that this is so. In this section there are described the structures of a number of compounds in the crystal lattices of which it is not possible to distinguish discrete molecules. In later chapters the shape of discrete molecules will be considered, but the ways in which these molecules are arranged in a crystal lattice lie outside the scope of the present work. The aim of this section is not to describe every known structure, but rather to select several which are important, to describe them in detail and to emphasise the underlying structural principles. Most of the structures to be described are adopted not just by one compound but by a large number of other compounds also, and an indication will be given in Chapter 4 of which other compounds adopt these various structures.

The compounds to be described are considered in two main groups, (1) binary compounds, and (2) ternary compounds, and each of these groups is subdivided further according to the stoichiometry of the compounds, i.e. the ratio of the number of atoms of one kind to the number of atoms of the other kind(s).

(1) Binary Compounds

Binary compounds are those which contain only two elements, and these are subdivided into sections according to whether their stoichiometry corresponds to (i) AB, (ii) AB_2, (iii) AB_3 and (iv) A_2B_3.

There are several factors which make a consideration of the structures of compounds different from a consideration of the structures of the metallic elements.

(*a*) There are two different types of atom.

(b) The atoms of the different elements usually differ from each other in size.

(c) The two elements generally differ from each other in electro-negativity (p. 21).

(d) Various stoichiometries have to be considered.

The different atoms must be bonded to each other in some way although for the moment the manner of this bonding need not be considered, and since there is probably a difference in the electronegativities of the different atoms it is reasonable to assume that the bonding electrons are not equally shared between atoms of the two different elements. Hence one type of atom can be regarded as bearing a small positive charge (not necessarily a formal unit positive charge as in a pure ionic bond) and this can be called the electropositive; the other atom must then bear a small negative charge and can be called the electronegative element. Considerations of electro-statics require that when a three-dimensional lattice is built up a positively charged atom will be surrounded by negatively charged atoms, and vice versa. Thus, in a compound $A_x B_y$ an atom of A will be surrounded by atoms of B and an atom of B by atoms of A, although the numbers of surrounding atoms will depend upon various factors among which is the stoichiometry of the compound, i.e. the values of x and y.

(i) Structures of some Compounds of Type AB

It is significant that very many compounds of type AB have one or other of five simple structures, and these will now be considered in turn. It should be pointed out that in the diagrams used to illustrate these and subsequent crystal structures, only the centres of the atoms are indicated, in order that the detail of the structure should be easily discerned. Another point which should be noted is that each Figure represents a small part of the structure, not necessarily a crystallographic unit cell, and this 'pattern' continues indefinitely in three dimensions as far as the boundaries of the crystal.

(a) The Sodium Chloride Structure   (Fig. 23)

The unit of this structure shown is a cube. Suppose that the atoms illustrated as ● are chlorine atoms and that those illustrated as ○ are sodium atoms. (The term ion might be used instead of the term atom, but the latter has been used since the precise nature of the chemical bonds has not been considered.) The arrangement of the chlorine atoms is seen to be face-centred cubic, i.e. the arrangement of cubic close-packing, since there are chlorine atoms at the corners of the cube and at the centre of each face. They would be truly close-packed only if they were in contact with each other, i.e. if the sodium atoms were sufficiently small not to push them apart. Consider the sodium atom marked '*A*' in the Figure; it is surrounded by six atoms of chlorine disposed towards the corners of a regular octahedron, and this is seen to be true for all the sodium atoms. Hence the sodium atoms can be regarded as being in octahedral sites in a cubic close-packed type of lattice of chlorine atoms. It has been seen previously (p. 51) that the requirement for precise fit in an octahedral site is a ratio of one radius to the other, in this case r_{Na}/r_{Cl}, of 0·414 and it

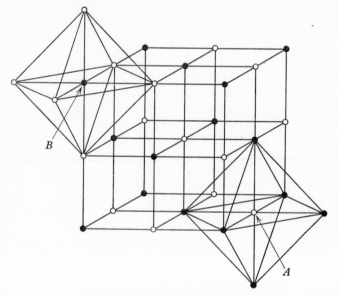

FIG. 23 The sodium chloride structure.

will be seen (p. 81) that this ratio is exceeded in the case of sodium chloride so that the chlorine atoms can not be in contact with each other. Hence the arrangement of the chlorine atoms is not really close-packing but will be called a close-packed type of arrangement since the geometry of the arrangement is the same as for true close-packing. All the octahedral sites are occupied since there is one octahedral site for every atom in a close-packed lattice (p. 50) and this corresponds to a 1:1 stoichiometry as is found in sodium chloride.

Further inspection of the Figure shows that the sodium atoms could equally well have been considered instead of the chlorine atoms since they can be seen to be entirely equivalent in their environment; an octahedral arrangement of sodium atoms round a chlorine atom is shown at 'B' in the Figure. There are thus three different ways in which the structure of sodium chloride can be described: (i) a cubic close-packed type of arrangement of chlorine atoms with sodium atoms filling all the octahedral sites; (ii) a cubic close-packed type of arrangement of sodium atoms with chlorine atoms filling all the octahedral sites; (iii) two interpenetrating cubic close-packed type of lattices, one of chlorine atoms and the other of sodium atoms. Of these three descriptions, the first is probably the best as it is most convenient to consider the larger atoms as being close-packed and the smaller as being in the interstitial sites, although it must be emphasised that all three descriptions are equally correct.

In the case of sodium chloride itself it would have been more correct to have described the structure as built of ions rather than of atoms since the compound is ionic, although other compounds which have this structure are not always ionic. Anions are usually larger than cations and in this example the chloride ion is larger than the sodium ion. Since each ion is surrounded by six ions of the opposite type in this structure the coordination is referred to as 6:6.

It may be useful to make a digression at this point to show how the number of 'molecules' in a unit of structure can be determined. A simple count in Fig. 23 reveals fourteen chlorine atoms and thirteen sodium atoms within the unit cube (i.e. omitting the additional atoms which are shown outside the cube and are only constructional aids), but this cube contains only four 'molecules' of NaCl.

The corner of a cube is shared among a total of eight cubes, so that an atom placed at a corner can contribute only $\frac{1}{8}$ to any given cube; the centre of an edge is shared among four cubes so that an atom placed there contributes only $\frac{1}{4}$ to a given cube; the centre of a face is shared by only two cubes so that an atom placed there contributes only $\frac{1}{2}$ to a given cube; an atom at the body centre of a cube contributes only to the one cube. When the chlorine atoms in Fig. 23 are counted there are eight at corners of the cube, $8 \times \frac{1}{8} = 1$, and six at face centres, $6 \times \frac{1}{2} = 3$, making a total of four. Counting the sodium atoms shows twelve at edge centres, $12 \times \frac{1}{4} = 3$, and one at the body centre $= 1$, again making a total of four; hence there are four atoms of each kind, or four 'molecules', in the cube corresponding to a stoichiometry of 1:1 in keeping with the formula NaCl.

(*b*) The Zinc Blende Structure   (Fig. 24)

As in the case of the sodium chloride structure which was described above, the unit illustrated is a cube. Let the atoms marked ● be sulphur atoms and the atoms o zinc atoms. The sulphur atoms are arranged in precisely the same way as were the chlorine atoms in the sodium chloride structure, that is a face-centred cubic or cubic close-packed type of lattice. Using the same reasoning as above, there must be four atoms of sulphur in the unit cube, and there are obviously four atoms of zinc within the cube so that again the stoichiometry is 1:1. In this structure, however, it can be seen that the zinc atom marked '*A*' in Figure 24 is surrounded by four sulphur atoms disposed towards the corners of a regular tetrahedron and not by six disposed octahedrally. Expressed otherwise, the zinc atoms occupy tetrahedral sites and have a coordination number of four. It can be seen that in this structure, as in the structure of sodium chloride, the two types of atom are equivalent as each sulphur atom is surrounded

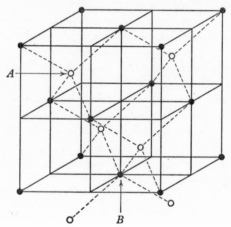

FIG. 24 The zinc blende structure.

tetrahedrally by four zinc atoms. Hence the zinc blende structure can be described in three different ways in an analogous manner to the three descriptions given for the structure of sodium chloride. The most convenient description is of sulphur atoms in a cubic close-packed type of arrangement with *half* the tetrahedral sites occupied by zinc atoms. Note the following points: (i) since there are two tetrahedral sites for every atom in a close-packed lattice (p. 49), the stoichiometry of the compound would be 1:2 if every site were occupied; only half the available tetrahedral sites are occupied in the structure of zinc blende. Compare Fig. 24 with Fig. 29, the structure of fluorite, in which every available tetrahedral site is occupied; (ii) the tetrahedral sites are occupied in a regular way, alternate sites being vacant; this also is best seen by comparing with Fig. 29;

(iii) the sulphur atoms would only be truly close-packed if they were in contact with each other, and for this to be so the ratio of the two radii, i.e. r_{Zn}/r_S would require to be 0·225 (p. 51) and it is appreciably larger than that.

The coordination of the zinc blende structure is described as 4:4.

(c) The Wurtzite Structure   (FIG. 25a)

This structure, which is an alternative form in which zinc sulphide occurs in nature, can be described as having sulphur atoms arranged in a hexagonal close-packed type of lattice with zinc atoms in half the tetrahedral sites. Hence it is very similar to the structure of zinc blende, differing only in the sequence in which the close-packed layers of sulphur atoms are arranged, i.e. they follow the sequence *ABABABA*, etc., in wurtzite and *ABCABCABCA*, etc., in zinc blende. As in the zinc blende structure the two types of atom are in equivalent positions, and the coordination is described as 4:4.

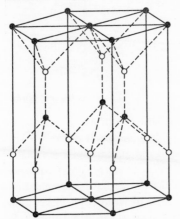
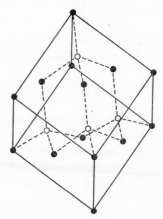

FIG. 25 (*a*) the wurtzite structure and (*b*) the zinc blende structure in a similar orientation.

The hexagonal close-packed type of arrangement of the sulphur atoms ● can be seen when Fig. 25a is compared with Fig. 15. It can also be seen that the zinc atoms ○ are in tetrahedral sites with four sulphur nearest neighbours, and similarly the sulphur atoms are tetrahedrally surrounded by zinc atoms although only the central layer of three sulphur atoms in the Figure illustrates this.

In Fig. 25b is shown the structure of zinc blende re-orientated so that the similarity between the structures of zinc blende and wurtzite can be

E

seen. (Fig. 25*b* bears the same relation to Fig. 24 as did Fig. 16*b* to Fig. 16*a*
see p. 47.)

(*d*) The Nickel Arsenide Structure   (Fɪɢ. 26)

This structure can be described as having arsenic atoms in a hexagonal
close-packed type of lattice with the nickel atoms occupying all the
octahedral sites.

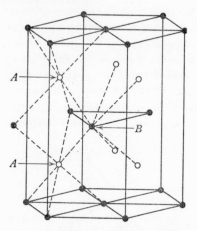

Fɪɢ. 26 The nickel arsenide structure.   Fɪɢ. 27 A trigonal prism.

It thus bears the same relation to the structure of wurtzite as did the
structure of sodium chloride to that of zinc blende. It differs from the
three structures which have been considered above, and from that of
caesium chloride (p. 60) in that the two types of atom are not in equivalent
sites. Whereas this structure can be described as having arsenic atoms
arranged in a hexagonal close-packed type of lattice with nickel atoms
occupying all the octahedral sites, the converse of this is not true. Reference to Fig. 26 shows that whereas a nickel atom o is surrounded octahedrally by six arsenic atoms, as shown at *A* in the Figure, an arsenic
atom • has the same coordination number of six, but the nickel atoms are
disposed towards the corners of a trigonal prism, as shown at *B* in the
Figure. A trigonal prism is shown in Fig. 27 and can be compared with
an octahedron as shown in Fig. 19*b* and described on p. 49; it can be
regarded as two equilateral triangles in parallel planes but with the
apices pointing in the same direction instead of in opposite directions as
in the case of the octahedron. The coordination of the nickel arsenide
structure is again described as 6:6. It is not possible to have a 6:6

coordinated structure based on hexagonal close-packing but with the two kinds of atom occupying equivalent positions.

In all the four structures described above, the coordination numbers of the atoms have been either four or six, and it has been shown how these coordinations can arise in close-packed lattices. Three other co-ordinations which are possible in close-packed lattices, i.e. 3-, 12- and 8-fold, are not found however in binary compounds of type AB, and these will be considered in turn.

(i) 3-fold coordination: this would necessitate placing an atom at the centre of an equilateral triangle of three close-packed atoms of the other element. The size of this site is very small indeed, presumably too small since there are no compounds of type AB known which have 3:3 coordination. Additionally, it might be expected that an atom in such a site would slip into an adjacent tetrahedral site which is both very near and larger than the three-fold site.

(ii) 12-fold coordination: this is the pattern of the coordination of the close-packed atoms themselves. If an atom of A is surrounded by twelve atoms of B, then each atom of B must be surrounded by twelve atoms of A for the compound to have a 1:1 stoichiometry, and this is clearly impossible. To show this, consider one plane of atoms only—12-fold coordination requires six of the nearest neighbours to be in one plane as was seen in the discussion on close-packing.

```
        ?     ?     ?
     ?     B     B     ?
  ?     B     A     B     ?
     ?     B     B     ?
        ?     ?     ?
```

Surround one atom of A with six atoms of B; then each atom of B has already two nearest neighbours which are atoms of B so that it cannot have six nearest neighbours which are atoms of A (see diagram). Twelve-fold coordination is possible in structures of different stoichiometry, and an example will be seen later—perovskite (p. 70).

(iii) 8-fold coordination: an atom in a close-packed lattice is surrounded by eight tetrahedral sites (see Fig. 29, fluorite), but an atom in a tetra-hedral site has only four-fold coordination so that eight-fold coordination is not possible in a compound of type AB although it is possible in one of type AB_2.

Hence no coordinations other than four or six are possible within a close-packed type of lattice for compounds of type AB, and the last structure of a compound of this stoichiometry to be described and which shows 8:8 coordination cannot be related to close-packing.

(e) The Caesium Chloride Structure   (FIG. 28)

This structure, like those of zinc blende and sodium chloride, is cubic. Chlorine atoms ● lie at the corners of a cube, and a caesium atom ○ is at the body-centre with eight chlorine nearest neighbours, as shown at *A* in the Figure. When the structure is extended as shown it can be seen that each chlorine atom is also surrounded by eight caesium atoms in the same arrangement (shown at *B* in the Figure) so that the two types of atom are in equivalent positions and the coordination is 8:8. It is incorrect to refer to this structure as body-centred cubic, since this term implies that the body-centre is occupied by the same kind of atom as that at the corners of the cube.

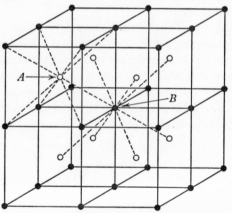

FIG. 28 The caesium chloride structure.

The interrelationship of various simple structures is summarised in Table VI; it is interesting to note that there does not seem to be any known example of a compound which has a structure corresponding to a hexagonal close-packed type of lattice with all the tetrahedral sites occupied.

TABLE VI

Sites filled	System of Close-packing	
	Cubic	*Hexagonal*
All octahedral	Sodium chloride	Nickel arsenide
Half tetrahedral	Zinc blende	Wurtzite
All tetrahedral	Fluorite	——

(ii) Structures of some Compounds of Type AB₂

Five examples of structures of compounds which correspond to the stoichiometry AB_2 will now be described. It is obvious that in these compounds the two kinds of atom must have different coordination numbers, which are in the ratio of 2:1. The coordinations of the first three structures to be described are 8:4, 4:2 and 6:3.

(a) The Fluorite Structure (CaF₂)   (FIG. 29)

This structure can be described as having calcium atoms in a cubic close-packed type of arrangement with fluorine atoms occupying *all* the tetrahedral sites.

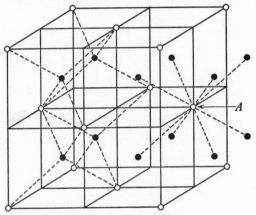

FIG. 29 The fluorite structure.

Reference to the Figure shows that the calcium atoms o are in a face-centred cubic or cubic close-packed type of arrangement; each fluorine atom ● is surrounded by four calcium atoms disposed tetrahedrally, and each calcium atom by eight fluorine atoms disposed towards the corners of a cube—the Figure has been extended beyond the cube boundary to illustrate this for the atom marked *A*. This structure is therefore an example of 8:4 coordination. It has been included in Table VI and can be compared with the structure of zinc blende, which has a cubic close-packed type of lattice with *half* the tetrahedral sites occupied.

It should be noted that it is the smaller cations which are in the close-packed type of arrangement and the larger anions which are in the so-called interstices. While this may seem strange, it must be remembered that when describing compounds of type AB as having the larger atoms in a close-packed type of arrangement, it was seen that the alternative description of the smaller atoms in this arrangement was no less valid (p. 55).

(b) The β-cristobalite Structure (one form of SiO₂)   (FIG. 30)

In this structure the silicon atoms comprise two interpenetrating cubic close-packed type of lattices, so arranged that an atom of the one lattice is surrounded tetrahedrally by four atoms of the other lattice. The oxygen atoms are then situated in positions midway between pairs of silicon atoms.

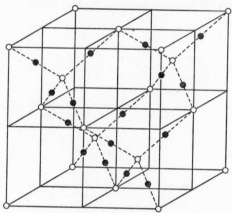

FIG. 30 The β-cristobalite structure.

The silicon atoms o are thus arranged to occupy the sites occupied by both zinc and sulphur atoms in the zinc blende structure. In this arrangement a silicon atom would have four nearest neighbours, but since oxygen atoms ● are sited between pairs of silicon atoms, it follows that a silicon atom has four oxygen nearest neighbours and that these are arranged tetrahedrally; an oxygen atom has two silicon nearest neighbours arranged linearly (this is only approximately true). Hence this structure has 4:2 coordination. (To simplify the description it was not pointed out earlier that the silicon atoms must be pushed apart when an oxygen atom is between two of them; this enlarges the lattice but without losing the overall cubic symmetry.)

(c) The Rutile Structure (one form of TiO₂)   (FIG. 31)

The unit of this structure is not a cube since one of the axes is shorter than the other two by about 30 per cent.; for convenience it will be described as a 'distorted' cube although it must be appreciated that the distortion is somewhat large.

The structure of rutile can then be described as a 'distorted' body-centred cubic arrangement of titanium atoms with oxygen atoms in positions of three-fold coordination.

Reference to Fig. 31 shows that each titanium atom ○, e.g. that marked *A*, is surrounded octahedrally by six oxygen atoms ●, and that each oxygen atom is surrounded by three titanium atoms disposed towards the corners of an equilateral triangle. The structure has thus 6:3 co-ordination.

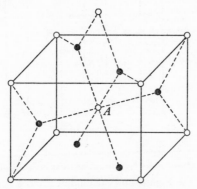

Fig. 31 The rutile structure.

Although this structure is not related to close-packing it has been related to a distorted body-centred cubic type of arrangement in order to suggest an approximation to close-packing (cf. the section on the structures of the metallic elements, p. 47, where it was seen that a body-centred cubic lattice was nearly as economical an arrangement as was close-packing). The occurrence of this type of three-fold coordination is also interesting since it is not very common in three-dimensional lattices and was not found in any compounds of type AB. There is another example of three-fold coordination in the structure of cadmium iodide described below, but in that case the three atoms are not disposed towards the corners of an equilateral triangle.

The calcium chloride structure is similar to the structure of rutile, but the octahedral coordination round the metal atoms is not regular. Whereas in the structure of rutile two of the axes of the unit cell are equal in length, all three axes of the unit cell of the structure of calcium chloride have different lengths; the coordination is the same as for rutile, i.e. 6:3.

(d) The Cadmium Iodide Structure (CdI$_2$)   (Fig. 32)

In this structure the iodine atoms are arranged in a hexagonal close-packed type of arrangement with cadmium atoms in octahedral sites only between every second two layers of iodine atoms.

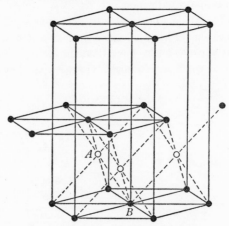

Fig. 32 The cadmium iodide structure.

Each cadmium atom o has six iodine nearest neighbours arranged octahedrally, see *A* in the Figure, and each iodine atom ● has three cadmium nearest neighbours, see *B* in the Figure, although these are *not* disposed towards the corners of an equilateral triangle as were the titanium atoms around an oxygen atom in the structure of rutile, discussed above. In this structure the three cadmium atoms form the base of a trigonal pyramid whose apex is the iodine atom. This can also be regarded as an octahedral arrangement (see Fig. 19*b*) with three adjacent corners of the octahedron unoccupied.

The arrangement of three layers I—Cd—I corresponds to a composition CdI$_2$, and since the positively charged cadmium atoms are sandwiched between layers of negatively charged iodine atoms, the outsides of the 'sandwich' are both negatively charged. When further layers of atoms are built up it is not possible to put a layer of cadmium atoms on top of the top layer of iodine atoms since the resultant arrangement, I—Cd—I—Cd, etc., corresponds to a stoichiometry of 1:1 instead of the required 1:2. So a layer of iodine atoms is placed on top of a layer of iodine atoms to give the arrangement I—Cd—I I, and when this is continued further it becomes

I—Cd—I I—Cd—I I—Cd—I, etc.

Since iodine atoms bear negative charges, this means that two negatively charged layers are adjacent to each other in the structure with no positively charged layer between them, so that it would not be expected that they would be held together as closely or as strongly as if there were a positively charged layer inserted between them. Thus the structure of cadmium iodide is referred to as a layer lattice and has relatively weak residual forces holding the I—Cd—I layers together. This has the effect of making the crystals of the compound flaky and easily cleaved.

In the structure of cadmium iodide the third layer of iodine atoms is directly above the first layer so that there is an *ABABABABA* type of arrangement of layers and the structure can be described as being related to hexagonal close-packing. The structure of cadmium chloride is closely related to that of cadmium iodide, the difference being that the chlorine atoms are arranged in an *ABCABCABCABCA*, etc., type of arrangement so that this structure can be described as being related to cubic close-packing, but it is, like cadmium iodide, a layer lattice.

Another important feature of the cadmium iodide structure is its relationship to the structure of nickel arsenide. This latter structure was seen to be derived by arranging arsenic atoms in a hexagonal close-packed type of lattice with nickel atoms occupying all the octahedral sites, i.e. between *every* pair of adjacent layers of arsenic atoms. In the cadmium iodide structure the iodine atoms are in the same hexagonal close-packed type of arrangement but with the cadmium atoms occupying octahedral sites only between *alternate* layers of iodine atoms, i.e. only half as many octahedral sites are occupied in the cadmium iodide structure as are occupied in the nickel arsenide structure. The similarity can be seen by comparing Fig. 32 with Fig. 26.

There are a number of cases known where the same two elements form compounds AB and AB_2, the former having the nickel arsenide structure and the latter the cadmium iodide structure. In these cases it is often found that a compound can be obtained which has got a composition which is intermediate between the two extremes, i.e. AB_x where $1 < x < 2$, and it can be appreciated that the structure is related to the structures of both cadmium iodide and nickel arsenide. In the structure of cadmium iodide the octahedral sites between every second pair of close packed layers are entirely vacant, whereas the corresponding sites in the nickel arsenide structure are entirely occupied; when the composition is intermediate, so too is the way in which these octahedral sites are occupied. Nickel and tellurium and cobalt and tellurium are pairs of elements which form compounds AB and AB_2 which adopt the nickel arsenide and the cadmium iodide structures respectively.

The structure of molybdenum disulphide is another example of a layer lattice, although the arrangement of the layers of sulphur atoms is *AAAAAA*, etc., and because of this the molybdenum atoms have the coordination of a trigonal prism instead of an octahedron as found in the cadmium halide structures.

(e) The Calcium Carbide Structure (CaC_2)   (Fig. 33)

This structure has been selected to illustrate an important point, that the structures of some compounds can be related to the structure of a compound which has a different stoichiometry; this shows the fundamental importance of several simple types of structure.

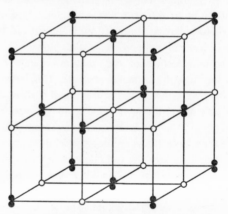

Fig. 33 The calcium carbide structure (ideally the cube should be elongated in the vertical direction).

The structure of calcium carbide can be compared with the structure of sodium chloride, the sodium and chlorine atoms being replaced by calcium and carbon atoms respectively; the carbon atoms are associated in pairs as shown in the Figure, and the C_2 groups are all aligned in the same direction, which means that the unit cell of the structure is distorted considerably from the cubic symmetry found in sodium chloride itself.

Two structures which are very similar to that of calcium carbide are those of the two forms of FeS_2, iron pyrites and marcasite. In these two structures, however, the S_2 units do not all align themselves in parallel.

Many other examples are known of compounds the structures of which can be related to those of simpler compounds, but where a polyatomic group replaces a single atom. Some examples of this are listed below:

(i) $BaSiF_6$ has the same type of lattice as caesium chloride, with the octahedral SiF_6 groups replacing the chlorine atoms.

(ii) $Ca(NO_3)_2$ has a fluorite type of lattice with the planar nitrate groups replacing the fluorine atoms.

(iii) K_2PtCl_6 has an anti-fluorite (see below) type of lattice; the fluorine atoms of the normal fluorite lattice are replaced by potassium atoms and the calcium atoms are replaced by octahedral $PtCl_6$ groups.

The prefix anti- is used to denote that the structure is reversed so that there are metal atoms in the sites where non-metal atoms are usually found, and vice-versa, in the manner indicated in example (iii) above. Simple examples are known, such as sodium monoxide, Na_2O, which has an anti-fluorite lattice. Anti-structures are only distinguishable if the two sets of atoms are not equivalent.

(iii) Structures of some Compounds of Type AB_3

Three examples of structure of compounds of type AB_3 will now be described.

(a) The Structure of Rhenium Trioxide (ReO_3)   (FIG. 34)

This structure can be described as having oxygen atoms occupying three-quarters of the positions in a cubic close-packed type of lattice (and is therefore further removed from true close-packing than are the previously described structures); rhenium atoms occupy one-quarter of the available octahedral sites.

The unit of structure shown in the Figure is a cube of oxygen atoms ● which is face-centred on only four of the six faces and which has rhenium atoms ○ on only four of the twelve edge centres. (This structure is sometimes shown in a different orientation such that an edge centre in this representation becomes a corner of the cube. Reference is made to this on p. 70 and the rather similar perovskite structure is shown in the two analogous representations in Fig. 35.) When the number of atoms in the unit cube is counted as was done for sodium chloride on p. 55, the 'real' content of the cube is seen to be one rhenium atom and three oxygen atoms, i.e. ReO_3. Each rhenium atom has six oxygen nearest neighbours arranged octahedrally, cf. A in Fig. 35a, and each oxygen atom has two

rhenium nearest neighbours arranged linearly. Thus the structure has
6:2 coordination; it should be compared with the structure of perovskite,
Fig. 35, in which the one in four vacant positions in the close-packed
lattice of oxygen atoms are occupied by atoms of a different element,
viz. calcium.

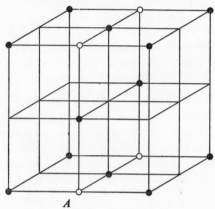

FIG. 34 The rhenium trioxide structure.

(b) The Structure of Bismuth Tri-iodide (BiI₃)

In this structure, which is a layer lattice, the iodine atoms are arranged
as in hexagonal close-packing with bismuth atoms occupying two-thirds
of the octahedral sites between alternate pairs of layers of iodine atoms.

This structure can be compared with that of cadmium iodide, the
difference being that in that structure cadmium atoms occupy all the
octahedral sites between alternate pairs of layers of iodine atoms. The
layers of iodine atoms are again in an *ABABABABA*, etc., arrangement
and hence there is a relationship to hexagonal close-packing. Whereas a
bismuth atom has an octahedral coordination, an iodine atom has only
two bismuth nearest neighbours in a non-linear arrangement. This should
be compared with the environment of the cadmium atoms in the structure
of cadmium iodide, described in detail on p. 64, but as there are only
two bismuth atoms in the structure of bismuth tri-iodide to occupy the
positions of three cadmium atoms in the structure of cadmium iodide,
and these are arranged in an ordered way, one of the three positions
forming the base of the trigonal pyramid (p. 64) is vacant, and the iodine
atoms have only two nearest neighbours; alternatively four adjacent
corners of the octahedron are unoccupied. The coordination of the
structure of bismuth tri-iodide is thus 6:2.

(c) The Structure of Chromium(III) Chloride (CrCl₃)

This structure is another layer lattice, and has chlorine atoms arranged in the pattern of cubic close-packing with the chromium atoms occupying two-thirds of the available octahedral sites between alternate pairs of layers of chlorine atoms. It thus bears the same relationship to the structure of bismuth tri-iodide as does the structure of cadmium chloride to that of cadmium iodide. The coordination of the structure is 6:2.

(iv) Structures of some Compounds of Type A_2B_3

(a) The Structure of Corundum (the most common form of Al_2O_3)

This structure has oxygen atoms arranged in a hexagonal close-packed type of lattice and aluminium atoms occupying two-thirds of the available octahedral sites.

An aluminium atom has thus six oxygen nearest neighbours arranged octahedrally, whereas an oxygen atom has four aluminium nearest neighbours disposed towards four of the six corners of a trigonal prism (see Fig. 27), so that the structure has a coordination of 6:4.

(b) The Structure of Manganese(III) Oxide (Mn_2O_3)

This structure has manganese atoms arranged in a cubic close-packed lattice with oxygen atoms occupying three-quarters of the tetrahedral sites.

It should be compared with the fluorite lattice, the calcium atoms being replaced by manganese atoms and three-quarters of the fluorine atoms being replaced by oxygen atoms, the remaining fluorine sites being left vacant. This structure also has a 6:4 coordination, but whereas the oxygen atoms have four manganese nearest neighbours arranged tetrahedrally the coordination of oxygen atoms around a manganese atom is less regular; it is such that six of the eight corners of a cube are occupied and the other two are unoccupied, and these two may be at the extremes of either a body diagonal or of a face diagonal, i.e. manganese atoms can occupy two different types of site in the lattice although both types of site have six-fold coordination.

It will be readily understood after reading the section (pp. 110-115) why the oxide of Mn(III) does not adopt the corundum lattice with its regular octahedral sites. Mn(III) has the electronic configuration d^4.

(2) Ternary Compounds

Finally, four examples of structures of ternary compounds will be considered, i.e. compounds which contain three elements and can be represented by the general formula $A_x B_y C_z$. These are the structures of the naturally occurring minerals perovskite, ilmenite, olivine and spinel, and these serve to illustrate that even more complicated structures can be described in terms similar to those which have been used for the description of simpler structures.

(a) The Structure of Perovskite (CaTiO₃)   (FIG. 35)

In this structure the calcium and oxygen atoms together comprise a cubic close-packed type of lattice, the calcium atoms being arranged in one-quarter of the positions in an ordered manner; the titanium atoms occupy one-quarter of the octahedral sites in the close-packed lattice.

Reference to Fig. 35a shows a cube with oxygen atoms ● at the corners and also at four of the six face-centres, and calcium atoms ◉ at the two remaining face-centres, so that the oxygen and calcium atoms together comprise a face-centred cubic or cubic close-packed type of lattice. The titanium atoms ○ occupy four of the edge centres (the other eight being vacant), and these are octahedral sites. Since a calcium atom is part of a close-packed lattice it has twelve oxygen nearest neighbours. A titanium atom has six oxygen nearest neighbours as illustrated at A in the Figure, whereas an oxygen atom has two titanium nearest neighbours arranged linearly and four calcium atoms only slightly further distant and disposed towards the corners of a square, so that the calcium and titanium atoms together comprise a distorted octahedron around an oxygen atom. An alternative representation of the structure of perovskite is shown in Fig. 35b. In this Figure the titanium atoms which are at the edge centres in Fig. 35a become the cube corners. This alternative representation shows the coordination of the three different types of atom more clearly although the relationship to a face-centred cubic arrangement is more easily seen in Fig. 35a.

The structure of perovskite is very similar to that of rhenium trioxide as a comparison of Fig. 35a with Fig. 34 shows. The difference is that the calcium atoms complete the close-packed lattice of oxygen atoms in the perovskite structure whereas this lattice is incomplete in the structure of rhenium trioxide. (As was pointed out on p. 67 the structure of rhenium trioxide can be redrawn so that it compares directly with Fig. 35b).

It can be seen that it is not possible to pick out discrete TiO₃ units in this structure as might be expected from the formula of the compound. Hence the name calcium titanate is not particularly appropriate for the compound since one would infer from that name the existence of titanate ions just as carbonate ions are found in the crystal structure of calcium

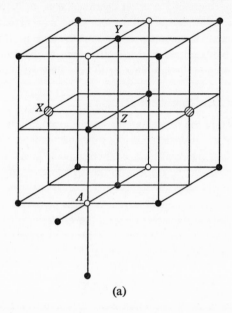

(a)

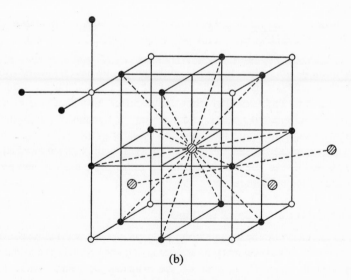

(b)

FIG. 35 The perovskite structure.

carbonate. The compound is better described as an oxide of calcium and titanium since the structure follows the same type of pattern as other oxide structures. These points apply equally well to the other three structures to be described in this section, and to the other compounds which will be seen in the next chapter to have these structures.

(b) The Structure of Ilmenite ($FeTiO_3$)

In this structure the oxygen atoms are arranged in a hexagonal close-packed type of arrangement with the iron and titanium atoms dispersed over two-thirds of the octahedral sites, presumably in an ordered manner.

Comparison should be made with the structure of corundum (p. 69) in which there are only aluminium atoms to occupy the same number of octahedral sites, i.e. $Fe + Ti = 2Al$. As in the perovskite structure there are no TiO_3 units in the structure, and the similarity of the structure to that of corundum emphasises that it is better to regard this compound also as an oxide rather than as a titanate.

(c) The Structure of Olivine (($Fe,Mg)_2SiO_4$)

In this structure the oxygen atoms are arranged in a hexagonal close-packed type of lattice with silicon atoms occupying one-eighth of the available tetrahedral sites and the metal atoms occupying one-half of the available octahedral sites.

In olivines the ratio of Fe:Mg can vary although the total $Mg + Fe$ must correspond to two atoms in the formula given above. This is the first structure described in this chapter in which atoms occupy both tetrahedral and octahedral sites, although in the perovskite structure positions of both six-fold and twelve-fold coordination are occupied by metal atoms. The interstitial atoms are dispersed throughout the oxygen lattice in an ordered manner, and since only a fraction of the available sites is occupied the interstitial atoms tend to be as far apart as possible. Hence an octahedral site immediately adjacent to an occupied tetrahedral site is left vacant. The olivine structure is rather too difficult to represent satisfactorily in a Figure.

(d) The Structure of Spinel (Al_2MgO_4)

In this structure the oxygen atoms are arranged in a cubic close-packed type of lattice with the metal atoms occupying one-eighth of the available tetrahedral sites and one-half of the available octahedral sites. The structure can therefore be compared to the structure of olivine which was based on a hexagonal close-packed type of lattice of oxygen atoms, in contrast to the cubic type of spinel.

The arrangement of the metal atoms is not always as straightforward as might be expected in the spinels. Consider the general formula A_2BO_4. Comparison with olivine would lead to a prediction that atoms of B would occupy tetrahedral sites and atoms of A octahedral sites. This is normally true, but there are compounds referred to as 'inverse spinels' in which one-half of the atoms of A are in the tetrahedral sites and the remaining half occupy octahedral sites as do the atoms of B. These are sometimes represented as $(AB)AO_4$ to illustrate this feature of their structure. An example of an inverse spinel is Fe_2MgO_4, or in the other representation $(Fe,Mg)FeO_4$.

Conclusions

Twenty or so different structures corresponding to different stoichiometries have now been considered and all possessed three-dimensional lattices in which it was not possible to pick out discrete molecules. The interrelationship of these structures to each other has been stressed, and the concepts of close-packing and interstitial sites have been seen to aid the descriptions of the various structures considerably. It should be emphasised again, however, that the lattices are only occasionally truly close-packed since the atoms in the interstitial sites are usually sufficiently large to push the host atoms apart.

4

FACTORS WHICH INFLUENCE
THE CRYSTAL STRUCTURE OF
THREE-DIMENSIONAL LATTICES

Introduction

In the preceding chapter the structures of a number of compounds were described, and these were selected as being important because in most cases a significant number of other compounds is known to have the same kind of atomic arrangement. For example, more than one hundred compounds are known to adopt the same structure as sodium chloride, perhaps the most common structure of all. In this chapter these various structures will be considered again to find out which compounds adopt the same types of lattice and this information will be used to elucidate some of the factors which influence structure. Particular reference will be made to compounds of the types AB, AB_2 and ABC_3.

(1) Binary Compounds

(i) Compounds of Type AB

The five structures which were described under this heading in the previous chapter will now be referred to again in the same order.

(a) The Sodium Chloride Structure (p. 53)

Most of the compounds which have the sodium chloride structure belong to one or other of the following three categories:

(i) compounds of the alkali metals and silver with the halogens and groups such as CN, OH and SH;

(ii) compounds of the alkaline earth metals and magnesium with the oxygen group of elements;

(iii) compounds of transition metals with small non-metallic elements such as carbon, nitrogen, oxygen, etc.

Some of the compounds in (iii) are among those referred to as interstitial compounds, and some examples of these are: TiC, VC, UC, NbN, CrN and PuO, etc. The precise nature of the bonding in these compounds is not too clearly understood, and they will not be considered further at this point. Compounds in (i) and (ii) are considered to have appreciable ionic character, and with the exception of silver the metals belong to the *s* block of the Periodic Table so that their ions have inert gas type of configurations.

(*b*) (*c*) The Zinc Blende and Wurtzite Structures (p. 55)

These structures are considered together as they are very similar to each other, and indeed a number of compounds have been found which are dimorphic and have both structures although under different conditions. Most compounds which have one or other (or both) of these structures belong to one or other of the following categories:

   (i) the cuprous halides;
  (ii) compounds of beryllium with the oxygen group of elements;
 (iii) compounds of zinc, cadmium and mercury with the oxygen group of elements;
  (iv) compounds of aluminium, gallium and indium with nitrogen, phosphorus, arsenic and antimony;
   (v) silicon carbide.

All the compounds in these different categories are considered to have appreciable covalent character. In categories (i), (ii) and (iii) all the metals with the exception of beryllium belong to the *d* block of the Periodic Table so that their ions do not have inert gas type of electronic configurations. Silicon carbide is a covalent compound and is isostructural with diamond. This is not surprising as silicon has the same electronic configuration as carbon in its outermost shell and there is not a big difference in electronegativity between the two elements. The compounds in (iv) would not be expected to have much ionic character since both cation and anion would have a charge of three units. It was seen in Chapter 1 that a highly charged cation would be highly polarising and a highly charged anion easily polarisable, and that polarisation leads to covalency.

It is a feature of inorganic compounds that when two compounds have the same number of electrons they often have the same structure (isostructural) and similar physical and chemical properties. The compounds are then said to be isoelectronic and those in (iv) and (v) above provide an example of this. Both carbon and silicon have four electrons in their outermost shells, whereas aluminium and its congeners on the one hand have three electrons and nitrogen and its congeners on the other have five, so that in each compound two atoms contribute eight electrons, which can be represented as:

$$Al(3) + N(5) = Si(4) + C(4) = 2C(4).$$

aluminium   silicon   carbon
nitride   carbide   (diamond)

In this case there is structural similarity although the chemical properties are not identical on account of the difference in electronegativity between the different elements in the compounds.

(d) The Nickel Arsenide Structure   (p. 58)

The nickel arsenide structure is adopted by compounds of the transition metals (except the copper and zinc groups) with sulphur, selenium and tellurium of the group six elements and arsenic, antimony and bismuth of the group five elements, but *not* with oxygen, nitrogen and phosphorus. Compounds with this structure are often non-stoichiometric, their actual composition often showing a variation from a precise 1:1 atomic ratio indicated by the formula. This occurrence of non-stoichiometry is more likely if the metal can exist in various oxidation states, since an excess or deficiency of the more electronegative element can be balanced by an increase or decrease respectively in the oxidation state of the metal so that the balance of electrical charge is not upset. It is a characteristic of most transition metals that they can readily exist in more than one oxidation state. The imperfections in a lattice which are necessitated by non-stoichiometry are more possible in covalent types of lattice than in ionic lattices. The similarity of the nickel arsenide structure to that of cadmium iodide (p. 65) facilitates non-stoichiometry.

(e) The Caesium Chloride Structure   (p. 60)

The caesium chloride structure is adopted by two categories of compound:

> (i) compounds of caesium, rubidium, thallium and ammonium with the halogens, etc.;
> (ii) a large number of intermetallic compounds.

Compounds of type (i) have appreciable ionic character and have very arge monovalent cations.

(ii) Compounds of Type AB_2

(a) The Fluorite Structure   (p. 61)

Compounds which have the fluorite lattice are the fluorides of divalent metals such as calcium, barium, lead and mercury, and the oxides of tetravalent metals such as cerium, zirconium and uranium. The non-metal atoms in these compounds are of the most electronegative elements, and they form anions which do not have large charges. The anti-fluorite lattice (p. 67) is found in compounds of the alkali metals with the oxygen group of elements, e.g. sodium monoxide, Na_2O. All these compounds have an appreciable degree of ionic character.

(b) The β-cristobalite Structure (p. 62)

This lattice is uncommon. Compounds with the same structure are beryllium fluoride and 'boron phosphate', BPO_4. This latter compound is another example of the isoelectronic principle referred to on p. 75, i.e.

$$B(3)+P(5)=2Si(4).$$

β-cristobalite is only one of several forms in which silicon dioxide can be obtained. The other forms have the same 4:2 coordination but have structures of lower symmetry.

(c) The Rutile Structure (p. 62)

Compounds which have the rutile lattice are, like those which have the fluorite lattice, fluorides of divalent metals, e.g. magnesium, nickel and zinc, and oxides of tetravalent metals, e.g. manganese and lead. The comments made in the section on fluorite are again applicable, although there does not seem to be any known example of a compound which has an anti-rutile lattice.

(d) The Cadmium Iodide and Cadmium Chloride Structures (p. 64)

Because of their similarity these two layer lattices can be considered together. They are found in compounds of the following categories:

(i) compounds of the transition metals with the halogens other than fluorine;
(ii) a number of hydroxides of divalent metals such as calcium, magnesium, iron, cobalt and nickel;
(iii) some sulphides, selenides and tellurides of transition metals, e.g. PtS_2, $NiTe_2$ and $TiSe_2$.

For compounds in category (i) the cadmium chloride structure is the more likely structure if the halogen is chlorine, whereas compounds in categories (ii) and (iii) have almost invariably the cadmium iodide structure. The iron pyrites structure (p. 66) is an alternative one for compounds of the type listed in (iii).

(e) The Calcium Carbide Structure   (p. 66)

The structure of calcium carbide (sometimes modified so that the C_2 units are not all in alignment) is found in a number of other metal carbides and in a number of compounds which contain the O_2^- or O_2^{2-} ions, e.g. potassium superoxide, KO_2, and barium peroxide, BaO_2.

Factors which Influence the Structures of Compounds AB and AB₂

Compounds of types AB and AB_2 will now be discussed together the arguments to be used are applicable to both equally. Firstly, however, it will be useful to recall the factors outlined on p. 24 which increase the covalent character of a compound which might be expected to be ionic, i.e. compounds formed between a metal on the one hand and a non-metal on the other. These factors are:

  (i) a small cation, since it is highly polarising;
 (ii) a large anion, since it is easily polarisable;
(iii) a high charge on either ion, since this makes a cation highly polarising and an anion easily polarisable;
(iv) a cation which does not have an inert gas type of electronic configuration, since the nuclear charge is less efficiently shielded in such an ion, and hence it is highly polarising.

Thus compounds tend to be ionic if the metal ion is large, has a low charge, usually $1+$ or $2+$, and has an inert gas type of electronic configuration, and if the electronegative atom is reasonably small and has a charge of $1-$ or $2-$. These conditions are fulfilled by the alkali and alkaline earth metals, and to a lesser extent by the smaller magnesium and beryllium, on the one hand, and by the halogens and the oxygen group of elements on the other. In the case of the electronegative non-metallic elements the tendency to form ionic compounds falls off quite rapidly in the following series:

fluorine > chlorine > bromine > iodine
oxygen > sulphur > selenium > tellurium
(fluorine > oxygen) > (chlorine > sulphur) > (bromine > selenium)
  > (iodine > tellurium)

Omitting the intermetallic and interstitial compounds, it can be seen that in most compounds which have either the sodium chloride or the caesium chloride structure the metal ions have an inert gas type of electronic configuration and do not bear a positive charge greater than two units. The non-metallic elements are without exception those in groups six and seven of the Periodic Table; i.e. these compounds have appreciable ionic character.

Most metal ions which are found to occur in compounds which have the zinc blende, wurtzite and nickel arsenide structures do not have inert gas type of electronic configurations, whereas the non-metallic elements are the less electronegative members of groups six and seven or the even less electronegative group five; i.e. these compounds have appreciable covalent character.

In the same way the compounds AB_2 in which the non-metal atoms are the most electronegative elements oxygen and fluorine are those which have the rutile and fluorite structures; i.e. these compounds are appreciably ionic even although the metal atom in most cases is one of the transition elements (see example (2) considered below). In contrast, the structures of cadmium chloride, cadmium iodide and pyrites are associated with compounds of the less electronegative non-metal atoms and hence they are appreciably covalent.

The generalisation can now be made that the structure of a compound is influenced by its degree of ionic or covalent character, the lattices of sodium chloride, caesium chloride, rutile and fluorite being associated with ionic character and those of cadmium chloride, cadmium iodide, pyrites, zinc blende, wurtzite and nickel arsenide with covalent character. It must also be appreciated that there is no sharp boundary between electrovalency (ionic bonds) and covalency.

Two examples will illustrate some of these points. (1) The structure of beryllium sulphide, BeS, is that of zinc blende, whereas magnesium sulphide, MgS, has the sodium chloride structure. The two metals are in the same group of the Periodic Table, and when ionised they have the same charge of $+2$; both ions have inert gas type of electronic configurations. The beryllium ion is appreciably smaller than the magnesium ion and this decrease in size associated with a positive charge greater than unity leads to an increase in covalency, so that beryllium sulphide is more covalent in character than magnesium sulphide and has a structure which is associated with covalent character whereas magnesium sulphide has a structure associated with ionic compounds.

The chemistry of zinc is often compared with that of magnesium since they are of comparable atomic and ionic size and show the same oxidation state in all their compounds. The difference in their chemistry is illustrated by the structures of their sulphides; the covalent nature of zinc sulphide is related to the non-inert gas type of electronic configuration of the zinc ion, in contrast to the ionic nature of magnesium sulphide since the magnesium ion has an inert gas type of configuration.

(2) Nickel fluoride, NiF_2, has the rutile structure whereas the other nickel halides have layer lattices. Two opposing effects make it difficult to predict the structure of nickel fluoride from first principles: (i) the electronic configuration of the nickel ion is not that of an inert gas, and this favours a covalent type of structure; (ii) fluorine is strongly electro-negative, and this favours an ionic type of structure; in addition, fluorine is a smaller atom (or ion) than chlorine and so the term 'r' (interionic distance) in the expression for the lattice energy is smaller for a fluoride than for a chloride, which makes the lattice energy larger for the fluoride, and hence an ionic fluoride is likely to be more stable than an ionic chloride, as it is likely to have a higher lattice energy. The second factor apparently outweighs the first since the structure of nickel fluoride is an ionic one. On the other hand, the lower electronegativity of chlorine and the other halogens (and their greater size) is insufficient to outweigh factor (i) above, with the result that nickel chloride has a covalent type of structure. The other nickel halides are even more covalent.

Similar reasoning can be used for the analogous case of nickel oxide, NiO, which has the sodium chloride structure whereas nickel sulphide, etc., have covalent lattices.

The next question to be considered is what determines whether a compound will adopt the structure of sodium chloride or caesium chloride, zinc blende or nickel arsenide, rutile or fluorite? Consider the first of these pairs, sodium chloride and caesium chloride. The significant feature to note at this point is that the compounds which have the caesium chloride lattice are those which contain the largest of the monovalent cations, e.g. caesium, rubidium, thallium and ammonium. It was seen that the structure of caesium chloride involves eight-fold coordination whereas that of sodium chloride involves six-fold coordination, and it can be appreciated easily that the larger an atom is, the greater the number of atoms of another kind that can be packed around it although the actual number will depend upon the size of the surrounding atoms; the larger the sur-rounding atoms are, the fewer of them can be arranged around a central atom. This can best be expressed in terms of *radius ratio*, which can be defined as 'the ratio of the radius of the cation to the radius of the anion'. (Since the structures under consideration are ionic, it is reasonable to use ionic rather than atomic radii, and hence to use cation and anion in the definition.) The larger the value of the radius ratio, the greater the number of anions that can surround a cation.

The Influence of Radius Ratio on Crystal Structure

When interstitial sites in close-packed lattices were described (p. 51), it was seen that an atom would fit exactly into an octahedral site if the ratio r_1/r_2 were exactly 0·414 (i.e. $\sqrt{2}-1$) and into a tetrahedral site if the ratio were 0·225. Hence geometrical considerations alone would suggest that a compound with a radius ratio of 0·414 would have the sodium chloride structure since the cations in this structure can be regarded as being situated in octahedral sites in a close-packed type of lattice of anions (p. 54). It can be shown also by simple trigonometry that when a cation is situated at the centre of eight anions disposed towards the corners of a cube as in the caesium chloride structure, the radius ratio for a perfect fit is 0·732 (i.e. $\sqrt{3}-1$), so that compounds with this radius ratio would be expected to have the caesium chloride structure. However, it is unlikely that all compounds will have a radius ratio which is one or other of these exact values.

Values of radius ratios are shown in Table VII for ionic compounds of type AB.

TABLE VII

	F	Cl	Br	I		O	S	Se	Te
Li	0·57	0·43	0·40	0·36	Mg	0·59	0·45	0·41	0·36
Na	0·72	0·54	0·50	0·45	Ca	0·80	0·61	0·56	0·50
K	0·98	0·73	0·68	0·62	Sr	0·95	0·73	0·66	0·59
Rb	0·91*	0·82	0·76	0·69	Ba	0·93*	0·82	0·75	0·67
Cs	0·79*	0·91	0·84	0·76					

Note.—Those values marked * are reciprocal values (i.e. r_2/r_1), which can be considered since the two types of ion are in equivalent sites in these lattices. The beryllium compounds are omitted since they have appreciable covalent character and have zinc blende and wurzite structures; this is presumably true of MgTe also.

All the compounds for which values are quoted in Table VII have the sodium chloride structure except magnesium telluride, which has the zinc blende structure, and caesium chloride, bromide and iodide, which have the caesium chloride structure. Although most of the values of radius ratio lie within the range 0·414–0·732 there are a number of compounds which have higher values.

It can be concluded that for values of radius ratio in the range 0·414–0·732 six-fold coordination is to be expected, and for values greater than 0·732 eight-fold coordination, although it is obvious that the caesium chloride lattice is not adopted by all the compounds for which it might be expected from these geometrical considerations, and indeed it is not found at a for any compounds which contain doubly charged ions. (Some of the compounds which have the sodium chloride structure at room temperature have the caesium chloride structure if they are allowed to crystallise at higher temperatures.) It is worth noting two points at this stage, however. Firstly, geometry is not likely to be the only consideration and allowance must be made in a more precise treatment for the gain in potential energy which arises when a number of oppositely charged particles are brought together in a crystal lattice, and this varies according to the particular type of structure. (This is the Madelung constant term in the expression for lattice energy (p. 20)). Secondly, ionic radius has no precise meaning so that conclusions which are based on it must not be expected to be completely rigorous.

On the whole, better agreement is obtained between radius ratio and predicted structure when compounds of type AB_2 are considered. There is a complicating factor, however, in that the higher charge on the cations leads to the adoption of the more covalent layer lattices by some compounds. Values for radius ratios are quoted in Table VIII for compounds formed between the group two elements and the halogens.

TABLE VIII

	F	Cl	Br	I
Mg	0·57 (6)	0·43 (6L)	0·40 (6L)	0·36 (6L)
Ca	0·78 (8)	0·59 (6)	0·54 (6)	0·49 (6L)
Sr	0·93 (8)	0·70 (8)	0·65 (Ir)	0·59 (Ir)
Ba	0·95* (8)	0·79 (Ir)	0·73 (Ir)	0·66 (Ir)

Notes.—   * Reciprocal value;
     (6) 6-fold coordination, ionic rutile type of lattice;
   (6L) 6-fold coordination, covalent layer lattice;
    (8) 8-fold coordination, ionic fluorite lattice;
   (Ir) an irregular structure, the coordination of which is difficult to define, but greater than six.

It can be seen that the more covalent layer lattices are adopted by the smaller cations and larger anions, as would be expected. The fluorite lattice is adopted by compounds where the radius ratio exceeds 0·70, and the rutile lattice for lower values. The existence of the irregular structure of some of the strontium and barium halides interferes somewhat with this regularity.

It was stated above (pp. 76, 77) that the fluorite and rutile structures are adopted by a number of fluorides and oxides of transition metals, and it was seen when considering the structures of nickel fluoride and nickel oxide (p. 80) that the tendency of the electronegative fluorine and oxygen

atoms to form ionic structures outweighed the tendency of the transition
metal ion to adopt a covalent lattice. In Table IX are listed values for the
radius ratio of some of these compounds.

TABLE IX

Fluorite		Rutile			
PbF_2	0·97	MnF_2	0·67	CoF_2	0·60
CdF_2	0·83	FeF_2	0·61	NiF_2	0·57
HgF_2	0·82	ZnF_2	0·60		
ThO_2	0·83	PbO_2	0·63	RuO_2	0·49
UO_2	0·79	SnO_2	0·56	TiO_2	0·48
CeO_2	0·77	MoO_2	0·51	VO_2	0·46
PrO_2	0·75	WO_2	0·51	MnO_2	0·39
ZrO_2	0·66	IrO_2	0·50		
HfO_2	0·65	OsO_2	0·50		

The transition from the fluorite to the rutile structure for oxides appears
to occur at a value of the radius ratio of 0·64, which is somewhat lower
than expected. However, the use of radius ratio as a criterion in predicting
the structure of an unknown compound is clear from the various examples
which have been considered in Tables VII-IX.

In compounds of greater covalent character there is more interaction
between the electrons of one atom and the electrons of another atom, so
that a treatment of structure which regards atoms as spheres and uses
only geometrical considerations to explain their structural arrangements
but does not take into account the spatial distribution of electrons is not
likely to be completely successful. For this reason, consideration of
whether a compound would be expected to adopt a tetrahedral arrangement, as in zinc blende and wurtzite, or an octahedral one, as in nickel
arsenide, must be deferred until a later chapter (p. 130 *et seq.*).

The factors which have been seen to be important in influencing structure in these compounds of types AB and AB_2 are

(*a*) the degree of ionic or covalent character of the compound;
(*b*) if the structure is ionic, the radius ratio or the relative sizes of the
two ions.

(iii) (iv) Compounds of Types AB_3 and A_2B_3

These will not be considered in detail. It is clear from the descriptions
of the structures that the layer lattices of chromium(III) chloride and

bismuth tri-iodide will be adopted by covalent compounds, and the structure of rhenium trioxide by compounds of more ionic character. Both the lattices of manganese(III) oxide and corundum are essentially ionic. The former is adopted particularly by the lanthanide oxides, and the latter by such oxides as those of iron(III) (ferric) and chromium.

(2) Ternary Compounds

(i) Compounds of Type ABC_3

Although the only structures which were considered for compounds of this type were those of ilmenite and perovskite, there are however many compounds which do not have either of these types of lattice; e.g. carbonates of divalent metals, and nitrates and chlorates of monovalent metals. In the structures of these compounds, discrete anions (the shapes of these will be considered in a later chapter) can be identified, and the arrangement of the two kinds of ion is often related to a simple lattice type (cf. pp. 66, 67). Examples of this are as follows:

NaCl type of lattice—$NaNO_3$, $CaCO_3$ (calcite), $NaClO_3$, $KBrO_3$.
NiAs type of lattice—KNO_3, $CaCO_3$ (aragonite), $PbCO_3$.
CsCl type of lattice—$NaIO_3$, NH_4NO_3.

Two points about the structure of compounds of the stoichiometry ABC_3 have to be considered. Firstly, what determines whether or not the structure of a given compound will contain discrete anions, and secondly, if the compound has a three-dimensional lattice in which no discrete anions can be detected, what influences whether it will adopt the structure of ilmenite or that of perovskite?

The compounds under consideration can be divided into two different categories, ABO_3 and $AB(hal)_3$, where 'hal' represents fluorine, chlorine or bromine. In these latter compounds element A usually has the oxidation state of $+1$, and element B of $+2$. It follows that atom A is probably larger than atom B as the lattice is an ionic one and ionic radii should be considered rather than atomic radii. In compounds of type ABO_3 there are three possibilities:

The oxidation state of A is $+1$, and that of B is $+5$.
The oxidation state of A is $+2$, and that of B is $+4$.
The oxidation states of both A and B are $+3$.

Again atom A (or ion) is usually the larger, since it is usually in the lower oxidation state.

Examples of compounds with the general formula ABC_3 are known in which element B is one or other of many different elements, but discrete ions $BC_3{}^{n-}$ are found in the structure only when element C is oxygen and element B is one of the following elements: boron, carbon, nitrogen, sulphur, chlorine and iodine and perhaps selenium and tellurium.

Of these elements, boron, carbon and nitrogen are very small atoms and no compounds are known in which they have a coordination greater than four (neither do they have the necessary orbitals to form more than four covalent bonds should the bonding be covalent, as will be seen in the next chapter), whereas in the structures of both ilmenite and perovskite element B has a coordination number of six. The remaining elements, i.e. sulphur, chlorine, iodine, etc., have larger atoms, but the halogens require to be in an oxidation state of $+5$ and the sulphur group elements an oxidation state of $+4$. If these elements are incorporated into an ionic lattice such as those of ilmenite and perovskite, they should be regarded as ions, and the loss of four or five electrons to form the appropriate ions would decrease the size of the atoms to such an extent that six-fold coordination would be most unlikely; the resultant highly charged and small ions would be so strongly polarising that the bonds would become covalent, and this is not in accord with an ionic structure.

It is concluded that discrete ions are unlikely in the structure of a compound ABC_3 if element C is a halogen, or if element C is oxygen unless element B is a non-metal which either has a small atom or is required to exist in a high oxidation state. It follows that the ilmenite and perovskite lattices are adopted by compounds in which element B is a metal; even in the case of metallic elements an oxidation state of $+5$ is uncommon and the ionic lattices are adopted more often by compounds in which element B has the oxidation states of either $+3$ or $+4$. A few compounds in which niobium and tantalum are present in the $+5$ state do adopt an ionic lattice, but these elements in that oxidation state have ions with an inert gas configuration and hence are not as strongly polarising as the halogens in the same oxidation state. Vanadium, the smaller congener of niobium and tantalum, is usually four-coordinate instead of six-coordinate and it has a tendency to form polyions rather than simple discrete anions.

The question of whether a compound adopts the perovskite or the ilmenite structure appears to be influenced by the ionic sizes of the three elements. To illustrate this, compounds in which element B is titanium and element C is oxygen, i.e. $ATiO_3$, will be considered. Wells has pointed out that when elements A and B fit exactly into their appropriate sites in the close-packed lattice of perovskite, the following expression is valid:

$$r_A + r_O = \sqrt{2}(r_B + r_O),$$

where r_A, r_B, and r_O are the ionic radii of elements A and B and oxygen respectively.

To show that this is so, consider the triangle enclosed by the points X, Y and Z in Fig. 35a. When all the atoms are in contact with each other, it can be seen that

$$XZ = YZ = r_B + r_O, \quad XY = r_A + r_O$$

and angle $XZY = 90°$.

$$\therefore \; XY^2 = XZ^2 + YZ^2, \text{ i.e. } (r_A + r_O)^2 = 2(r_B + r_O)^2$$

$$\text{or } r_A + r_O = \sqrt{2}(r_B + r_O).$$

It follows that if this condition is fulfilled, a given compound will have the perovskite structure. Experience suggested that the above formula should be modified by the inclusion of a 'tolerance factor' t, so that the equation becomes

$$r_A + r_O = t\sqrt{2}(r_B + r_O).$$

It is not unreasonable that there should be some tolerance since the alternatives available to an atom of A are 12-fold or 6-fold coordination and the appropriate sites for these coordinations differ in size by a factor of more than two.

Wells suggested that the perovskite structure, or a slight distortion of it, is adopted by a given compound when $0.8 < t < 1.0$, but that when $t < 0.8$ the ilmenite structure is preferred. In table X are shown the values of t for the various titanium compounds under consideration.

TABLE X

Perovskite Structure		Ilmenite Structure	
Element A	t	Element A	t
Ba	0·99	Cd	0·84
Pb	0·95	Mn	0·80
Sr	0·93	Co	0·77
Ca	0·86	Fe	0·77
		Mg	0·76
		Ni	0·76

There is reasonable agreement between the values shown and the structures found for the compounds, although the cadmium compound might have been expected to have the perovskite structure.

Another example which shows the influence of ionic size on the structures of compounds of the stoichiometry ABC_3 can be taken from the compounds in which element B is niobium, and element A is an alkali metal. The compounds $NaNbO_3$ and $KNbO_3$ both have the perovskite structure, whereas $LiNbO_3$ which contains the smaller lithium ion has the ilmenite structure.

The Tungsten Bronzes

While considering the perovskite lattice, some comment should be made on the structure of the so-called tungsten bronzes. These materials, which are of variable composition, are obtained when sodium tungstate is treated with reducing agents at high temperatures and they correspond to the formula Na_xWO_3, where $0.3 < x < 1.0$. When $x = 1$, the oxidation state of the tungsten atom is $+5$, and if x were zero it would be $+6$ and the compound would become WO_3. Hence when the composition is intermediate there must be present in the lattice tungsten atoms in both $+5$ and $+6$ oxidation states.

When the composition corresponds to $NaWO_3$ (i.e. $x = 1$), the structure is that of perovskite with sodium atoms (ions) occupying all the available sites of 12-fold coordination. At the other extreme of composition the compound becomes WO_3 if x were 0, and this compound has the structure of rhenium trioxide (ReO_3) which was seen on p. 70 to be the same as the perovskite structure but with all the sites of 12-fold coordination vacant. Intermediate composition, i.e. $0.3 < x < 1.0$ therefore corresponds to an appropriate fraction of the sites of 12-fold coordination being occupied by sodium atoms, but the lattice of tungsten and oxygen atoms remains unchanged whatever the composition.

The colour of $NaWO_3$ is described as golden-yellow, and as the sodium content (x) falls the colour changes from yellow through red and violet to blue, and hence the name of tungsten bronzes for the 'compounds'. Another characteristic property of the tungsten bronzes is that they possess high electrical conductivity presumably due to the existence in the lattice of tungsten atoms in two different oxidation states.

(ii) Compounds of Type A_2BC_4

A large number of compounds is known which correspond to the general formula A_2BC_4, but since element C is almost invariably oxygen (it can also be sulphur and certain of the halogens) consideration will be limited to A_2BO_4. As was the case with compounds of general formula

ABO_3 there are three possible combinations of the oxidation states for elements A and B. These are:

The oxidation state of A is $+1$, and that of B is $+6$.

The oxidation state of A is $+2$, and that of B is $+4$.

The oxidation state of A is $+3$, and that of B is $+2$.

In addition to the structures of olivine and spinel which were considered in the previous chapter, there are other lattices known for compounds of type A_2BO_4, and two of these can be referred to briefly. Firstly, the structure of phenacite, Be_2SiO_4, has a three-dimensional lattice of oxygen atoms which are not in close-packing, with atoms of both beryllium and silicon in tetrahedral coordination. Secondly, there are a number of closely related structures such as those adopted under different conditions by potassium sulphate (i.e. polymorphism) in which discrete SO_4^{2-} anions can be recognised.

It appears that structures which contain discrete anions are found only for compounds in which element B has an oxidation state of $+6$ (with the exception sometimes of silicon which is $+4$). Probably the only elements in this category are the non-metals sulphur, selenium and tellurium and the metals chromium and manganese, which are the smallest elements in their respective groups. This situation can be compared with that found in the previous section for compounds ABO_3, where discrete ions were seen to be likely when element B is a non-metal, and the behaviour of the small vanadium atom can be compared with that of chromium and manganese.

It is less easy to predict which of the other structures would be expected for a given compound, although it can be said that the spinel lattice is much more common than that of olivine, and that the phenacite lattice in which there are no six-fold sites, is found when element A is rather small.

Interrelationship of the Structures of Iron Oxides

When the structures of the iron oxides are compared, an interesting relationship is found. The structure of FeO is that of sodium chloride, i.e. oxygen atoms in a cubic close-packed type of lattice with the iron atoms in octahedral sites. The structure of Fe_3O_4 is that of spinel, i.e. a cubic close-packed type of lattice of oxygen atoms with the iron atoms in both tetrahedral and octahedral sites, the formula of the compound being represented as $Fe_2^{III}Fe^{II}O_4$. The structure of $\gamma-Fe_2O_3$ is closely related to that of spinel (the more usual $\alpha-Fe_2O_3$ has the corundum structure). If a spinel structure is represented as $A_6B_3O_{12}$, atoms A and B will occupy six octahedral and three tetrahedral sites, i.e. a total of nine sites. $\gamma - Fe_2O_3$ becomes Fe_8O_{12} so that there are only eight atoms to be distributed randomly over the nine possible sites.

It is possible to oxidise Fe_3O_4 to $\gamma - Fe_2O_3$ under carefully controlled conditions, and the reverse process can be brought about by heating *in vacuo*. A mechanism for the sequence of oxidations $FeO \rightarrow Fe_3O_4 \rightarrow \gamma - Fe_2O_3$, or perhaps more clearly $Fe_{12}O_{12} \rightarrow Fe_{12}O_{16} \rightarrow Fe_{12}O_{18}$, can now be seen. As oxidation takes place, oxygen atoms approach the lattice and gain electrons released by the process $Fe^{2+} \rightarrow Fe^{3+} + e^{-1}$, thereby becoming oxygen ions and these add on to the lattice in the same cubic close-packed type of arrangement. The iron atoms (ions) then redistribute themselves as required in different sites in the now enlarged lattice.

Conclusions

In summary, some of the factors which must be considered when predicting a structure for a given compound are:

(i) the stoichiometry of the compound;
(ii) whether the bonding is covalent or ionic;
(iii) the relative sizes of the constituent atoms;
(iv) whether the atoms are of metals or non-metals, i.e. basic or acidic.

Some further considerations will be developed in the following chapters.

5

THE STRUCTURES OF COMPOUNDS WHICH CONTAIN COVALENT BONDS—PART I

Introduction

It was seen in the preceding chapters that the structure of a compound which is predominantly ionic in character can be derived by considering the most economical way in which its constituent ions can be packed together, allowing for their relative sizes and the stoichiometry of the compound. It was seen also that a consideration of size alone was not sufficient to decide the likely structure of compounds of appreciable covalent character. Covalency requires an overlap of orbitals of different atoms to allow the formation of electron pair bonds, so that if bonds are formed between an atom of A and several atoms of B then the atoms of B must approach the atom of A in such directions as suitable orbitals of the atom of A are to be found; otherwise no overlap is likely, and hence no covalent bond formation. The important features to which consideration must be given, therefore, are the appropriate orbitals of the atom of A, and the number of atoms of B which are covalently bonded to it.

The structures of compounds which contain covalent bonds (and in this category are included the structures of polyatomic ions) will be treated under three headings, each of which forms the subject matter of one chapter:

(i) discrete molecules and ions in which the central atom occurs in either the *s* or the *p* block of the Periodic Table;
(ii) discrete molecules and ions in which the central atom occurs in the *d* block of the Periodic Table;
(iii) polynuclear molecules and ions and three dimensional covalent structures in which no discrete molecules or ions can be detected.

The Stereochemistry of s and p Block Elements

In 1940 Sidgwick and Powell pointed out in the Bakerian lecture that elements which have the same grouping of electrons in their outermost or valency shell have the same stereochemistry, i.e. the same spatial arrangements of bonds; this stereochemistry can often be deduced by making the simple assumption that electron pairs repel each other and therefore orientate themselves in such a way as to be as far apart in space as possible; this observation applies whether an electron pair constitutes a covalent bond or remains as a non-bonding pair of electrons sometimes known as a 'lone pair'.

In Table XI are listed the directional properties which have been observed experimentally for the various numbers of pairs of electrons. It can be seen that the geometry of the arrangements found for five and seven pairs does not correspond with the above assumption.

TABLE XI

No. of electrons in shell	No. of pairs of electrons	Arrangement of pairs round the nucleus	Angle subtended at the nucleus by adjacent pairs
4	2	linear	180°
6	3	triangular planar	120°
8	4	tetrahedral	109° 28′
10	5	trigonal bipyramidal	120° and 90°
12	6	octahedral	90°
14	7	pentagonal bipyramidal	90° and 72°

Two points should be noted. Firstly, a square planar disposition of four electron pairs which might have been expected results in an angle of only 90° being subtended at the nucleus by two adjacent electron pairs, so that the electron pairs are further apart in a tetrahedral arrangement. Secondly, whereas the geometrical arrangements for 2, 3, 4 and 6 electron pairs are highly symmetrical, and in each case all the electron pairs are equivalent in that the same angle is subtended at the nucleus no matter which two pairs of electrons are chosen, the arrangements for 5 and 7 electron pairs are less symmetrical and the electron pairs are not all equivalent. This can be seen by reference to Fig. 36. A trigonal bipyramid comprises an equatorial plane which is an equilateral triangle, with apices above and below this plane, and although five electron pairs arranged in this way may be equidistant from the nucleus, it can be seen that the angle subtended at the nucleus by electron pairs at B and C is 120° whereas that subtended by pairs at A and B is 90°. A pentagonal bipyramid can be described similarly except that the equatorial plane is a regular pentagon instead of an equilateral triangle, and hence the angle subtended by the two points on the equatorial plane is 72° instead of 120°.

The structures of simple molecules and ions can now be considered according to the number of electrons contained in the valency shell of the central atom in each case.

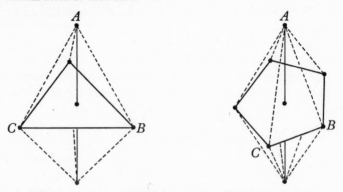

FIG. 36 (*a*) a trigonal bipyramid and (*b*) a pentagonal bipyramid.

Four Electrons—Quartet

A valency shell of only four electrons is uncommon, although reference will be made in Chapter 6 (p. 120) to some examples which are compounds of the zinc and copper groups of elements in the *d* block. The only elements in the *s* and *p* blocks which might be expected to have a two covalent quartet (i.e. a quartet of electrons which is used in forming two covalent bonds) are those of group II of the Periodic Table, and in particular the smallest and most covalent member of this group, beryllium. Whereas some compounds of beryllium may be monomeric in the gaseous state, e.g. $BeCl_2$, they tend to polymerise in the solid state since this allows the beryllium atoms to approach an inert gas type of configuration.

Consider a molecule of beryllium chloride, $BeCl_2$. The electronic configuration of a neutral beryllium atom in its ground state, considering only the outermost or valency shell, is $2s^2$, and that of a chlorine atom is $3s^2 3p^5$. A convenient convention for representing electronic configurations which will be used throughout this text is shown below for these two atoms.

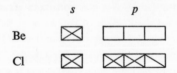

Each 'box' represents an orbital, and so can accommodate two electrons; the electrons are represented by the diagonal lines, crossed lines denoting an electron pair.

Each chlorine atom has one unpaired electron and is able to form one covalent bond by pairing this electron with one unpaired electron of another atom. The beryllium atom, however, does not have any unpaired electrons and can only acquire them if the two paired s electrons can be unpaired and one of them promoted to the p level which is a level of higher energy. Although energy must be supplied to the beryllium atom to raise it to this higher energy state, this is more than offset by the energy released when two covalent bonds are formed by pairing electrons with the unpaired electrons of two chlorine atoms. The configurations of the beryllium atom before and after bonding to the two chlorine atoms are therefore as shown:

	s	p
Beryllium atom in ground state	⊠	☐☐☐
Beryllium atom in excited state	◩	◩☐☐
Beryllium atom having gained two electrons from chlorine atoms	⊠	⊠☐

The beryllium atom now has two pairs of electrons and these are disposed as far apart as possible thus making an angle of 180° at the nucleus, and since the electron pairs are forming bonds, the molecule of $BeCl_2$ is a linear one, Cl—Be—Cl.

Six Electrons—Sextet

This valency group is somewhat more common than a quartet and is found in certain covalent compounds of boron and its congeners. Consider the molecule of boron trifluoride, BF_3. The electronic configuration of a neutral boron atom in its ground state is $2s^2 2p^1$ and that of a fluorine atom is $2s^2 2p^5$. The boron atom, in the ground state, has only one unpaired electron, i.e. the $2p$ electron, so that to allow the boron atom to form three covalent bonds the two $2s$ electrons must be unpaired and one of them promoted to the $2p$ level (cf. beryllium above). The electronic configurations of the boron atom before and after bonding to three fluorine atoms are as shown:

	s	p
Boron atom in ground state	⊠	◩☐☐
Boron atom in excited state	◩	◩◩☐
Boron atom having gained three electrons from fluorine atoms	⊠	⊠⊠☐

Thus the boron atom in the molecule of boron trifluoride has three pairs of electrons and these are disposed as far apart as possible, making a

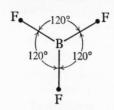

triangular planar arrangement with the boron nucleus at the centre, and since the electron pairs are forming bonds, the molecule of BF_3 is planar with a F—B—F bond angle of 120°, see Fig. 37.

FIG. 37 The shape of a molecule of boron trifluoride.

Similarly, the other boron halides and alkyls have planar molecules. The corresponding aluminium compounds also have a planar structure when they are monomeric, but many of these dimerise in such a way that the aluminium atom becomes four covalent (cf. p. 134). The borate ion, BO_3^{3-}, is also planar. A molecule of boric acid, $B(OH)_3$, if it can exist as a discrete molecule, would be isoelectronic with the molecule of boron trifluoride, and thus would be isostructural with it. The borate ion is derived from this hypothetical molecule by the removal of three hydrogen ions, i.e. three protons, which leaves the electronic configuration unchanged, so that the residual borate ion must, like the boron trifluoride, molecule, be planar, see Fig. 38.

FIG. 38 A 'molecule' of boric acid and the borate ion.

A somewhat different example is provided by stannous chloride, $SnCl_2$, which forms monomeric molecules in the gaseous state. The electronic configuration of a neutral tin atom in the ground state is $KLM4s^24p^64d^{10}5s^25p^2$, or, considering only the valency shell, s^2p^2. Thus it has two unpaired electrons with which it can form two bonds with chlorine atoms and by forming two bonds it acquires a sextet:

	s	*p*
Tin atom in ground state	⊠	◩◩▢
Tin atom having gained two electrons from chlorine atoms	⊠	⊠⊠▢

This sextet is, however, two-covalent and not three-covalent as is the sextet of electrons on the boron atom of boron trifluoride. It was pointed out (p. 91) that the electron pairs are to be regarded as repelling each other in the same way whether they are bonding or non-bonding, so that a bond angle of 120° would be expected in this molecule as in boron trifluoride, with the lone pair of electrons occupying the third position of the equilateral triangular arrangement as shown in Fig. 39.

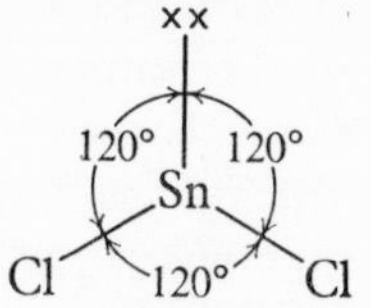

The bond angle would be exactly 120° only if the repulsive force exerted by a non-bonding pair of electrons is the same as that exerted by a bonding pair. Experimental evidence, however, suggests that a non-bonding pair of electrons exerts a stronger repulsive force than a bonding pair, so that in a molecule which contains both, the bonding pairs will be pushed a little closer together than the simple argument above would predict, with a corresponding decrease in bond angle. The bond angle in the stannous chloride molecule should therefore be less than 120°.

FIG. 39   The Approximate shape of a stannous chloride molecule.

Eight Electrons—Octet

This is the most common valency group for s and p block elements. It was seen in Table XI (p. 91) that the disposition of four electron pairs is towards the corners of a regular tetrahedron. Examples of compounds in which the central atom has a four-covalent octet as its valency group include compounds of the Group IV elements, e.g. CF_4, SiH_4, $GeCl_4$ and SnI_4. As in the case of boron trifluoride which was considered above, the two s electrons of the group IV element require to be unpaired in order to provide four unpaired electrons for covalent bond formation. Thus, the electronic configuration of a silicon atom is s^2p^2 in the ground state; to enable it to form four covalent bonds with, for example, chlorine atoms the two s electrons must be unpaired as shown:

	s	p
Silicon atom in ground state		
Silicon atom in excited state		
Silicon atom having gained four electrons from chlorine atoms		

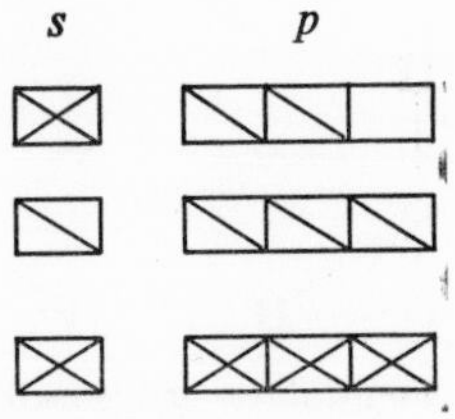

The formation of four covalent bonds gives the silicon atom a four-covalent octet so that the electron pairs and hence the bonds are arranged tetrahedrally around the central silicon atom.

Not only does an individual atom have a tetrahedral stereochemistry, but in compounds which have chains of carbon or silicon atoms, e.g. the paraffins and the silanes, the structure of the molecule is such that each atom of carbon or silicon is surrounded tetrahedrally. When the central atom is bonded to four atoms which are not identical, e.g. in the molecule $CHClF_2$, the bond angles are not all equal to the regular tetrahedral angle of $109° 28'$. The bonds to different atoms differ in length so that the electron pairs can be regarded as being at different distances from the nucleus of the central atom. Hence their repulsive forces and, in consequence, the bond angles in the molecule must vary slightly.

Further examples of molecules whose stereochemistry is that of a four-covalent octet and are thus tetrahedral are afforded by compounds in which elements of groups I-III have gained an inert gas type of configuration by acting as acceptors, e.g. $F_3B{\leftarrow}O(C_2H_5)_2$, the addition compound formed by boron trifluoride and ether, in which the valency group of the boron atom is increased from a sextet to an octet by accepting an electron pair from the oxygen atom, i.e. a dative covalent bond. There are a number of ions also which have this valency group on the central atom and are thus tetrahedral, e.g. the isoelectronic series SiO_4^{4-}, PO_4^{3-}, SO_4^{2-}, ClO_4^-; BeF_4^{2-} and BF_4^- which are isoelectronic with the molecule CF_4; NH_4^+ which is isoelectronic with the molecule CH_4.

In addition to being four-covalent, octets can be three- or two-covalent. The electron pairs are again disposed tetrahedrally around the nucleus of the central atom, but since only three or two of the pairs respectively are used in forming bonds, one or two of the corners of the tetrahedron are occupied not by atoms but only by lone pairs. The structures of the resultant molecules can be described as pyramidal, since the three bonded atoms form the base of a pyramid, and non-linear respectively; the structures of molecules based on the three types of octet are shown in Fig. 40.

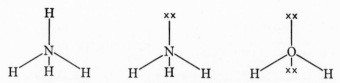

FIG. 40 Four-, three- and two-covalent octets—the tetrahedral ammonium ion, the pyramidal ammonia molecule and the non-linear water molecule.

Examples of molecules whose stereochemistry is based on three-covalent octets are to be found in compounds of the group V elements, e.g. NH_3, NCl_3, PH_3 and PF_3 and also in the ions SO_3^{2-} and ClO_3^{-}. The structures of all these species are pyramidal, and as expected from the discussion above (see under $SnCl_2$) the bond angles are less than the regular tetrahedral angle. Examples of two-covalent octets are to be found in compounds of the group VI elements, e.g. H_2O, H_2S, OF_2, SCl_2, etc., and in the ion ClO_2^{-}. The shapes of these species are all non-linear in contrast to the linear arrangement which is found for atoms with a two-covalent quartet.

Ten Electrons—Decet

Valency groups which are larger than the octet must use d orbitals in addition to s and p orbitals. When it is necessary to unpair electrons and to promote one or more to a higher energy level in order to have the correct number of unpaired electrons available for bond formation, the d level is used immediately after the p level in sequence. This is in contrast with the order in which the various energy levels are filled in simple atoms where a p level is always followed by an s level, in order of increasing energy (p. 4). A consideration of the molecule of phosphorus penta-fluoride, PF_5, will illustrate these points.

The neutral phosphorus atom has the configuration $3s^2 3p^3$ in its valency shell, and in order to provide five unpaired electrons for bond formation the s electrons must be unpaired and one of them promoted to a higher level. Each p orbital is singly occupied so that the level used is the $3d$ not the $4s$, whereas the potassium atom has the configuration $3s^2 3p^6 4s^1$, i.e. in the neutral potassium atom in its ground state the $4s$ level is next in energy after the $3p$. When five electron pair bonds are formed with five fluorine atoms the phosphorus atom has a decet, and as was seen in Table XI, the shape assumed by the molecule is that of a trigonal bi-pyramid (Fig. 36).

	s	p	d
Phosphorus atom in ground state	☒	⧄⧄⧄	☐☐☐☐☐
Phosphorus atom in excited state	◩	⧄⧄⧄	⧄☐☐☐☐
Phosphorus atom having gained five electrons from fluorine atoms	☒	☒☒☒	☒☐☐☐☐

The structures of all the phosphorus pentahalides when they are monomeric are trigonal bipyramidal, but in the solid state both phosphorus pentachloride and pentabromide adopt quite different structures which reflect the difficulty of packing economically in space trigonal bipyramidal arrangements of atoms, on account of the low symmetry. The structure of solid phosphorus pentachloride is built of PCl_4^+ and PCl_6^- ions (arranged as in the CsCl lattice); in the former ion the phosphorus atom has a four-covalent octet and the structure is accordingly tetrahedral, whereas in the latter it has a six-covalent duodecet and the ion is octahedral (see below); both these shapes are of higher symmetry than the trigonal bipyramid and hence are more easily packed in a crystal lattice. The structure of solid phosphorus pentabromide, in contrast, is built of PBr_4^+ and Br^- ions.

It was seen above (p. 91) that all five corners of a trigonal bypyramid are not equivalent, so that the stereochemistry of two-, three- and four-covalent decets can not be predicted unambiguously. For example, in a four-covalent decet, the non-bonding pair of electrons could occupy an apex or an equatorial position of a trigonal bipyramid, so that in theory at least, isomerism is possible. The structure of those compounds which have been determined experimentally show that in all cases the two apices of the bipyramid are occupied by atoms whereas the non-bonding pair(s) of electrons occupy the equatorial positions. Examples of molecules whose structures are based on a valency group of a decet are not very common; the sulphur atom in the molecule of sulphur tetrafluoride, SF_4, has a four-covalent decet, the chlorine atom in the molecule of chlorine trifluoride, ClF_3, has a three-covalent decet (the central atoms in the molecules PF_5, SF_4 and ClF_3 are isoelectronic), and the iodine atom in the ion ICl_2^- has a two-covalent decet. The structures of these are shown in Fig. 41; that of the ion ICl_2^- is linear, that of chlorine trifluoride is T-shaped and that of sulphur tetrafluoride can be compared to a see-saw of which the sulphur atom is the pivot, two of the fluorine atoms form the base and the remaining two are the seats at the extremities of the plank.

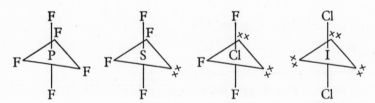

FIG. 41 Five-, four-, three- and two-covalent decets—the trigonal bipyramidal phosphorus pentafluoride molecule, the 'see-saw' shaped sulphur tetrafluoride molecule, the T-shaped chlorine trifluoride molecule and the linear dichloroiodate ion.

Twelve Electrons—Duodecet

A compound whose stereochemistry is based on a duodecet as the valency group is sulphur hexafluoride, SF_6. This can be considered in the same way as was phosphorus pentafluoride above:

	s	*p*	*d*
Sulphur atom in ground state	⊠	⊠◺◺	☐☐☐☐☐
Sulphur atom in excited state	◺	◺◺◺	◺◺☐☐☐
Sulphur atom having gained six electrons from fluorine atoms	⊠	⊠⊠⊠	⊠⊠☐☐☐

The sulphur atom is seen to have a six-covalent duodecet and so the shape of the molecule is that of a regular octahedron with the sulphur atom at the centre and the six fluorine atoms at the corners. The ions PF_6^- and SiF_6^{2-} which are isoelectronic with the molecule of sulphur hexafluoride are further examples of this valency group and therefore have octahedral structures.

The iodine atom in the molecule of iodine pentafluoride, IF_5, has a five-covalent duodecet as its valency group and that in the ion ICl_4^- has a four-covalent duodecet. Since all the six corners of a regular octahedron are equivalent, the structure of the IF_5 molecule must be a square pyramid with the lone pair of electrons occupying the remaining apex of the octahedron, Fig. 42. Two corners of a regular octahedron can be selected in two different ways—they can be either adjacent or diametrically opposite. In the structure of the ion ICl_4^- two diametrically opposite apices are occupied by non-bonding pairs of electrons so that the arrangement of the chlorine atoms is that of a square plane, Fig. 42.

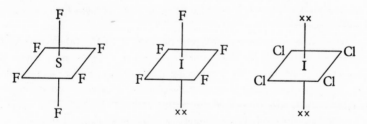

FIG. 42 Six-, five- and four-covalent duodecets—the octahedral sulphur hexafluoride molecule, the square-based pyramidal iodine pentafluoride molecule, and the planar tetrachloroiodate ion.

Fourteen Electrons—Quatuordecet

The only known compound whose stereochemistry is based on this valency group is iodine heptafluoride, IF_7.

	s	p	d
Iodine atom in ground state	⊠	⊠⊠	☐☐☐☐☐
Iodine atom in excited state	☐	☐☐☐	☐☐☐☐
Iodine atom having gained seven electrons from fluorine atoms	⊠	⊠⊠	⊠⊠☐

The iodine atom is seen to have a seven-covalent quatuordecet and the shape of the molecule is that of a pentagonal bipyramid, Fig. 36.

Hybridisation

In Chapter 1 the angular probability distributions of the various orbitals were described and it was pointed out that the one atom would form a covalent bond with a second atom only if the latter approached in the appropriate direction to allow interaction of electrons, or more precisely overlap of orbitals. In this chapter so far, the shapes of molecules and ions have been discussed without making any reference to the angular probability distributions of the individual orbitals used by the elements in compound formation. Thus in the molecule of sulphur hexafluoride, for example, which was considered above, it was seen that the sulphur atom uses for covalent bond formation electrons which are in s, p and d orbitals and these have quite different spatial characteristics. None the less the shape of the molecule is regular and all six bonds are equivalent, which leads to the conclusion that not only the bonds but also the six orbitals of the sulphur atom are equivalent. For this to be so, the six appropriate orbitals of the sulphur atom must be 'scrambled' in order to produce six 'new' orbitals all of which are equivalent and can be used for compound formation.

This discussion could equally well be applied to the other molecules whose structures have been considered above. Fortunately, there is theoretical justification for considering that orbitals can be 'scrambled', and the process is referred to as *hybridisation of orbitals* and the 'new' orbitals which are produced are called *'hybrid' orbitals*. The spatial characteristics of the hybrid orbitals are quite different from those of the simple orbitals from which they were derived.

Consider the simplest example of hybridisation, the combination of an *s* and a p_x orbital to form two *sp* hybrid orbitals. The angular dependence of these is shown in Fig. 43. It can be shown that, as a result of the symmetry of the individual *s* and *p* orbitals, their combination must produce two new orbitals which are concentrated along the *x* axis as shown in the Figure, and that two bonds formed by electrons in these hybrid orbitals are collinear.

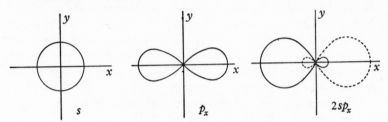

FIG. 43 The angular dependence of *sp* hybrid orbitals.

The relative orientations in space of several different combinations of orbitals have been calculated and are shown in Table XII.

TABLE XII

Hybrid orbitals	Distribution round atomic nucleus
sp	linear
sp²	triangular planar
sp³	tetrahedral
sp³d	trigonal bipyramidal
sp³d²	octahedral
sp³d³	pentagonal bipyramidal or face-centred octahedral*
sp²d	square planar

* Depending upon which *d* orbital is used in the hybridisation.

The distributions in space of the various hybrid orbitals immediately recall the distributions which were obtained on the assumption that electron pairs are situated as far apart in space as possible in order to minimise their repulsive forces upon each other, see Table XI, p. 91. When reference is now made to the compounds which were used to illustrate the above discussion, it is seen that when the valency group of an element is a quartet, an *s* and a *p* orbital are occupied, i.e. *sp* hybrid orbitals are used in bond formation, and not one *s* orbital and one *p* orbital; when the valency group of an element is a sextet, one *s* and two *p* orbitals are occupied, i.e. sp^2 hybrid orbitals are used in bond formation; an octet requires the use of sp^3 hybrid orbitals, a decet sp^3d, a duodecet sp^3d^2, and a quatuordecet sp^3d^3 hybrid orbitals.

No examples are known of compounds in which an s or p block element uses sp^3d^3 hybrid orbitals to obtain a face-centred octahedral arrangement, or sp^2d hybrid orbitals to obtain a square planar arrangement; the square planar arrangement found in the ion ICl_4^- is obtained by the use of sp^3d^2 hybrid orbitals since the valency group of the iodine atom is a duodecet.

If atoms of B are to form covalent bonds with an atom of A they must approach that atom along the direction in which the appropriately hybridised orbitals are directed, and a consideration of the hybridisation of orbitals used by the central atom (of an element in the s or p block) of a compound or ion will lead to a correct prediction of the structure of that species.

Multiple Bonds

Before concluding this chapter some consideration must be given to the formation of multiple bonds and the effect of these on the stereochemistry of the molecules concerned. In all the molecules considered so far the bonds have been electron pair covalent, or dative covalent, bonds, but many covalent molecules contain multiple bonds. As an example of one such molecule, consider ethylene, C_2H_4.

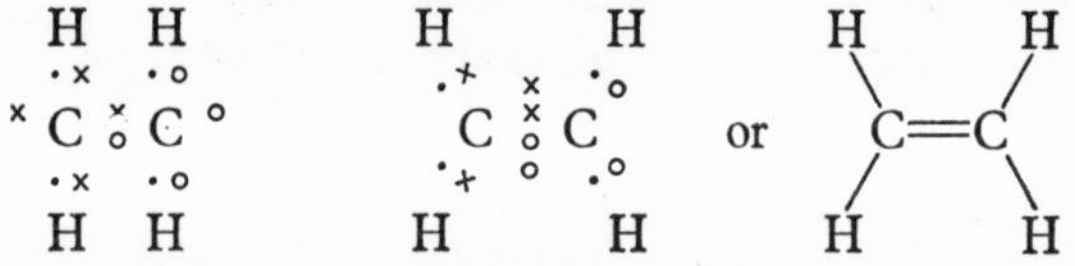

FIG. 44 The ethylene molecule.

In the molecule of ethane, C_2H_6, each carbon atom has a four-covalent octet and thus uses sp^3 hybrid orbitals in forming a tetrahedral arrangement of bonds. In the ethylene molecule, however, each carbon atom is bonded to only three other atoms, one carbon and two hydrogen. If this is written in the conventional way using electron pair bonds, Fig. 44a, each carbon atom has only seven electrons, and since molecules with unpaired s or p electrons are uncommon, and an inert gas type of electronic configuration can be attained by both carbon atoms if the two 'odd' electrons are shared, the molecule is written as in Fig. 44b with four electrons shared between the two carbon atoms, and this is called a double bond.

A theoretical justification for this representation in which four electrons are shared between two atoms comes from a consideration of the orbitals which are used by the atoms. Suppose that each carbon atom forms three electron pair bonds with other atoms, then:

Carbon atom in ground state

Carbon atom in excited state

Carbon atom having gained three electrons from other atoms

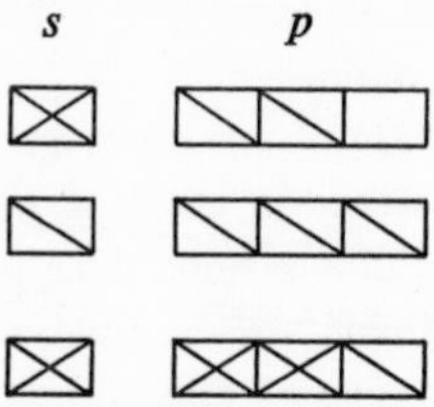

Each carbon atom has then a three-covalent sextet and one additional electron. Three sp^2 hybrid orbitals are used in bond formation so that a triangular planar arrangement of bonds (and hence of bonded atoms) is obtained around each carbon atom. For convenience (though it is an arbitrary choice), suppose that the two p orbitals used are the p_x and the p_y, then the sp^2 hybrid orbitals are concentrated in the xy plane, and the 'odd' electrons (i.e. those which are unpaired in the above representation) are situated in the p_z orbitals.

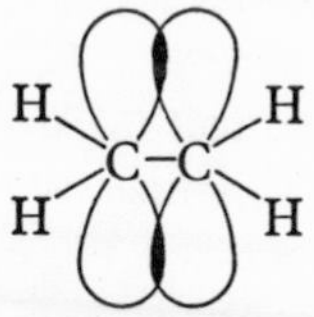

FIG. 45 The ethylene molecule showing the overlap of orbitals to form a π bond (the C and H atoms are coplanar and lie in a plane at right angles to the plane of the paper).

In Fig. 45 the molecule of ethylene is shown 'sideways-on' with the hydrogen atoms slightly displaced since the carbon and hydrogen atoms are all coplanar. The p_z orbitals are shown, but not the sp^2 hybrid orbitals which are concentrated in the xy plane. It can be seen that the p_z orbitals overlap both above and below the line which joins the two carbon nuclei and this is a different mode of overlap from that encountered previously, where the overlap of orbitals is along the line joining the nuclei of the two atoms. This overlap of orbitals which contain unpaired electrons results in an interaction between them so that a bond is formed, and the ethylene molecule has no unpaired electrons as can be determined by measuring its magnetic moment (p. 38). This type of bond where the orbital overlap is above and below the line joining the nuclei is known as a π bond, whereas when the overlap is between the nuclei the bond is known as a

σ bond. The two carbon atoms in the ethylene molecule are thus held together by a σ bond and a π bond.

The molecule of acetylene, C_2H_2, contains a triple bond, i.e. six electrons are shared between the two carbon atoms. Each carbon atom forms two σ bonds, one to a hydrogen atom and the second to the other carbon atom, using sp_x hybrid orbitals; the p_y and the p_z orbitals of the carbon atoms overlap to form two π bonds at right angles to each other and also to the σ bond.

The formation of a π bond draws atoms together more closely, so that the C—C distance in ethylene where the two carbon atoms are bonded by both a σ and a π bond is 15 per cent. shorter than the corresponding distance in ethane, for example, where there is only a σ bond. It is clear from the example of ethylene which has just been considered that the shape of a molecule or ion is determined by the number of σ bonds (and of non-bonding pairs of electrons) that it contains and is not affected in any way by formation of π bonds, although the π bonds lead to a shortening of the interatomic distances. Some examples will now be considered to illustrate the stereochemistry of molecules which contain double bonds.

In the molecule of carbon dioxide the carbon atom forms double bonds with both oxygen atoms, i.e. it is written as O=C=O. The carbon atom forms two σ bonds and two π bonds and has no non-bonding pairs of electrons; the orbitals used in forming two σ bonds must be sp hybrids so that the structure of the molecule is linear. Nitrous oxide, which can be written as N⇌N=O, is isoelectronic with carbon dioxide and must also be a linear molecule.

The molecule of sulphur dioxide can be written either as O=S̈=O or O=S̈→O, and both these representations satisfy valency requirements. In each the sulphur atom forms two σ bonds, as did the carbon atom in carbon dioxide, and in addition it has a non-bonding pair of electrons. The difference between the two representations is that in the one the sulphur atom forms two π bonds and in the other it forms only one. In order to accommodate the lone pair the sulphur atom must use three sp^2 hybrid orbitals, one of which is occupied by the lone pair and the other two are used in forming σ bonds with the oxygen atoms; thus, the bond angle O—S—O should be somewhat less than 120° (cf. $SnCl_2$, p. 94), in contrast to the O—C—O bond angle of 180° in the molecule of carbon dioxide. It is important to realise that both representations of the molecule shown above lead to the same conclusion that the molecule is non-linear, and that from a stereochemical point of view it does not matter whether the sulphur atom forms one or two π bonds. In fact, the electronic configuration of the molecule is probably intermediate between the two representations shown above, which makes it difficult to illustrate in a diagram.

To amplify this last comment, consider the second representation of the molecule shown above in which the sulphur atom forms a dative bond with one of the oxygen atoms. The sulphur, which is the donor atom, acquires a positive charge and the oxygen atom as the acceptor acquires a negative charge, but as pointed out on p. 15 the molecule tends to minimise this separation of charges if this is possible in any way. Now, the p orbitals of the oxygen atom which contain lone pairs of electrons will be near in space to the empty $3d$ orbitals of the sulphur atom (the electronic configuration of a sulphur atom is $KL3s^2 3p^4$), and if some overlap can occur (see Fig. 46) between an occupied p orbital of the oxygen atom and an unoccupied d orbital of the sulphur atom a π bond results.

FIG. 46 A dative π bond formed between empty $3d_{xy}$ orbital of a sulphur atom and the filled p_y orbital of an oxygen atom.

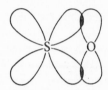

Since both the electrons constituting this bond originate on the one atom, i.e. the oxygen atom, it is known as a dative π bond. If the two electrons of this bond are then equally shared between the two atoms, this would correspond to a complete transference of one electron from oxygen to sulphur and so the separation of charges would be nullified completely. The two atoms are then held together by a dative σ bond from the sulphur to the oxygen and a dative π bond from the oxygen to the sulphur, and if the electrons are equally shared this corresponds exactly to the first representation of the molecule as given above. As the oxygen atom has a greater electronegativity than the sulphur atom, the electrons will on average be nearer to the oxygen atom than to the sulphur atom, so that there will be at least a partial negative charge on the oxygen atom; thus it has been shown that the two representations of the molecule are extremes and that the true picture is somewhere between these. Since both representations predict the correct shape of the molecule it does not seem to matter for present purposes which is used.

There are many other molecules and ions in which a bond can be written as double or single as in the above case, for example the ions $SO_4{}^{2-}$ and $SO_3{}^{2-}$ which were referred to previously, and it seems that this

H

type of dative bond is formed whenever possible and results in a strengthening of the σ bond which already exists between the two atoms and a shortening of the bond length.

The molecule of sulphur trioxide can be derived from that of sulphur dioxide by using the lone pair of electrons on the sulphur atom to form a dative covalent bond to the additional oxygen atom. This is a σ bond so that the sulphur atom in the molecule of sulphur trioxide forms three σ bonds; the electronic configuration around the sulphur atom is the same as around the sulphur atom in the molecule of sulphur dioxide so that again sp^2 hybrid orbitals are used and each of these forms a bond; the three bonds, and therefore the molecule, are thus seen to be planar.

The molecule of thionyl chloride, $SOCl_2$, can be written as

$$\begin{array}{ccc} \text{O} & & \text{O} \\ \uparrow & & \parallel \\ \text{Cl—S—Cl} & \text{or} & \text{Cl—S—Cl} \\ \ddot{} & & \end{array}$$

and thus the sulphur atom forms three σ bonds and in addition has a non-bonding pair of electrons. It therefore uses four sp^3 hybrid orbitals which are disposed tetrahedrally so that the molecule is pyramidal (cf. NH_3), with the lone pair occupying the apex of the tetrahedron around the sulphur atom. The molecule of sulphuryl chloride, SO_2Cl_2, can be derived from that of thionyl chloride in exactly the same way as the molecule of sulphur trioxide was derived from that of sulphur dioxide above, and hence it must be a tetrahedral molecule. Another tetrahedral molecule which is somewhat similar is that of phosphorus oxychloride, $POCl_3$.

It was seen on p. 97 that the chlorate ion, ClO_3^-, has a pyramidal structure; in contrast the nitrate ion, NO_3^-, is planar. In order to see why these ions should have different structures consider first the nitrate ion. Nitric acid is formulated as

$$\begin{array}{c} \text{O} \\ \diagup\!\diagup \\ \text{H—O—N} \\ \diagdown\!\diagdown \\ \text{O} \end{array}$$

and when a proton is ionised off to leave the nitrate ion the electronic arrangement is unchanged, so that the nitrogen atom forms three σ bonds and one π bond. This is precisely the same environment of a carbon atom in the ethylene molecule (p. 102), and the orbitals used are the same, i.e. sp^2 hybrids so that the nitrate ion is planar with bond angles of 120°. (The carbonate ion CO_3^{2-} is isoelectronic with the nitrate ion and so is also planar.) The chlorine atom in the chlorate ion has a three-covalent octet for its valency group, i.e. it forms three σ bonds and has a non-bonding pair of electrons also, and thus uses sp^3 hybrid orbitals and this leads to the pyramidal structure observed for that ion.

As a final example, the molecule of borazole, $B_3N_3H_6$, can be considered. It can be seen by reference to Fig. 47a that each boron atom and each nitrogen atom forms three σ and one π bond, the nitrogen atoms being donors and the boron atoms acceptors of the dative bonds. The orbitals used by both the boron and the nitrogen atoms must be sp^2 hybrids (cf. the nitrogen atom in the nitrate ion and the boron atom in boron tri-fluoride) which are at an angle of 120° to each other. The arrangement of boron and nitrogen atoms therefore becomes that of a regular hexagon and is planar. The six p_z orbitals of the atoms which constitute the ring are at right angles to the plane of the ring and accordingly each overlaps

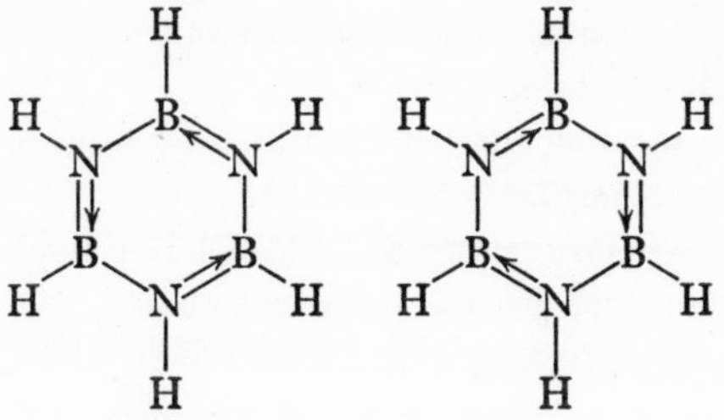

(a)   (b)

FIG. 47 The molecule of borazole.

with its two neighbours in the same way as the p_z orbitals of adjacent carbon atoms in the ethylene molecule overlap with each other; thus all six orbitals are interconnected and the π electrons are not localised but are free to travel around the entire ring. The alternative representation of the molecule shown in Fig. 47b leads to precisely the same picture and the two representations are therefore equivalent.

Boron nitride, BN, is analogous to borazole, but as there are no hydrogen atoms the structure becomes an infinite two-dimensional sheet with each nitrogen atom bonded to three boron atoms and each boron atom to three nitrogen atoms. The boron—nitrogen bond is isoelectronic with the C—C bond,

$$B(3)+N(5)=2C(4),$$

so that the structure of benzene is the same as that of borazole, except that the π bond is not dative, and similarly the structure of graphite, one modification of carbon, is the same as the sheet structure described above for boron nitride. Recently, also, a second form of boron nitride has been synthesised and this has the tetrahedral structure found in diamond, the second modification of carbon (see Chapter 7, p. 129).

Summary

To summarise, the following procedure can be adopted to derive the stereochemistry of an s or p block element in a particular compound:

(1) Write down the formula of the compound showing σ bonds, π bonds, and non-bonding pairs of electrons.

(2) Determine the size of the valency group by counting the number of electrons used in σ bond formation or which remain as non-bonding pairs, but omitting those used in π bond formation.

(3) Halve this number to find the number of orbitals required; choose the required number of orbitals starting with the s, up to three p, and thereafter d orbitals.

(4) Determine the directions adopted by these orbitals after hybridisation by consulting Table XII, p. 101.

(5) Arrange the bonded atoms and non-bonding electron pairs (if any) in these directions around the central atom.

6

THE STRUCTURES OF COVALENT
COMPOUNDS—PART II

The Stereochemistry of the d Block Elements

The approach which was developed in the previous chapter to gain an understanding of the stereochemistry of the s and p block elements is inadequate when applied to the elements of the d block. An important feature which contributes to this inadequacy was pointed out in Chapter 1, p. 10, where it was seen that all five d orbitals are not equivalent, in contrast to the equivalence of the three p orbitals.

The five d orbitals can be divided into two sets, see Fig. 5; the first set comprises the $d_{x^2-y^2}$ and the d_{z^2} orbitals, and these are referred to as the d_γ orbitals; the maxima in their angular probability distributions coincide with the x, y and z axes, and in this respect they resemble the p orbitals. The second set comprises the d_{xy}, d_{yz} and the d_{zx} orbitals, and these are referred to collectively as the d_ϵ orbitals, their angular probability distributions are a maximum at an angle of 45° to each axis and are zero along the three axial directions.

In considering the stereochemistry of s and p block elements, those valency group electrons which form σ bonds or remain as non-bonding pairs are all allocated to hybridised orbitals, so that a non-bonding pair of electrons is regarded as occupying a position in space which is equivalent to that occupied by a bonding pair. In the d block elements only the one set of the d orbitals is normally used in hybridisation, and the alternative set can accommodate the non-bonding electrons, which therefore do not occupy positions equivalent to those of the bonding pairs They are located in directions intermediate between the hybrid orbitals, and their effect on the stereochemistry of molecules and ions is limited to the distortion of symmetry and to the destabilisation of particular configurations, as will be seen later.

With the exception of iodine heptafluoride, no molecules are known in which an atom of an s or p block element has more than four d electrons in an unfilled shell and hence may require to use both sets of d orbitals; it was also noted in Chapter 1 that unpaired electrons are uncommon in compounds of s and p block elements although found in such molecules as NO, NO_2 and ClO_2. In contrast, many atoms of the d block elements can have more than four d electrons in an unfilled shell, and unpaired electrons are frequently found in the non-bonding orbitals.

The effect of these differences between Main Group and Transition elements is best approached by a consideration of the Ligand Field Theory.

The Ligand Field Theory

This theory regards the transition metal atom, which is the central atom in a molecule or ion, as a positive ion surrounded by negatively charged atoms or groups of atoms, which are referred to as ligands*, even when the bonding between the central atom and the ligands is known to be appreciably covalent. The theory thus describes the situation within the molecule or ion from an extreme point of view and gives no information whatever about the orbitals which are used in bonding; as will be seen, however, the results of its application are very valuable.

The theory considers the effect of the electrostatic field due to the ligands upon the energy levels of the d orbitals of the central metal atom. Since the surrounding atoms or groups, i.e. ligands, are considered to be negatively charged, the electrons of the central atom will be subjected to repulsive forces which are strongest in the directions along which the ligands approach. The d electrons, which on account of the non-equivalence of their orbitals can be regarded as having some choice in the matter, will tend to occupy those orbitals which are furthest removed from the directions of approach of the ligands; that is to say, the energy of those orbitals which point in the same direction as the approach of the ligands is increased by that approach. The most common arrangements of ligands around a central atom are octahedral and tetrahedral, and the effect of ligand fields of these symmetries will be considered in turn.

Octahedral Ligand Field

When six ligands are disposed octahedrally around a central atom they approach that atom along the directions of the x, y and z axes, i.e. the precise directions along which the d_γ orbitals of the central atom are concentrated. (Fig. 48 shows the coincidence of the three axial directions with the corners of a regular octahedron.) The electrostatic field associated with the six ligands varies in strength according to the chemical nature

---

* Sometimes the ligands are neutral molecules, e.g. NH_3 and H_2O; these are polar and have dipole moments, the negative end of the dipole being directed towards the metal ion.

of the ligands, and it is customary to consider separately the effect of weak fields and the effect of strong fields. A weak ligand field is one which has no great effect upon the relative energies of the two sets of d orbitals, and the electrons fill these in the normal way, i.e. no d orbital is doubly occupied until all the others are singly occupied, in accordance with Hund's rule (see Chapter 1, p. 12). If, however, there is a strong electrostatic field associated with the ligands, then an electron in a d_γ orbital of the central atom would be acted upon by a strong repulsive force, and this causes the electron(s) to occupy the d_ε orbitals rather than the d_γ orbitals even although this does involve a breakdown of Hund's rule.

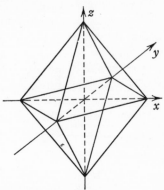

FIG. 48 The correspondence of a regular octahedron with the x, y and z axial directions.

Expressed differently, the d_γ orbitals are said to be destabilised with respect to the d_ε orbitals since their energy has become so high compared with that of the d_ε orbitals that the electrons are forced to occupy the latter, which are not directed along the lines of approach of the ligands, so that the electrons in the d_ε orbitals are not subjected to the same repulsive force. The different effects of strong and weak fields can be illustrated by means of an example.

The electronic configuration of a neutral iron atom is $4s^2 3d^6$ and that of a ferric ion, i.e. iron in the oxidation state of $+3$, is $4s^0 3d^5$.* In accordance with Hund's rule the five d electrons occupy separate orbitals as shown in Fig. 49. When six ligands approach the iron atom octahedrally and exert only a weak field, the energy of the d_γ orbitals is not appreciably altered with respect to the energy of the d_ε orbitals, so that the five electrons remain in the same orbitals as they occupy in the free ion, i.e. each d_γ and d_ε orbital is singly occupied. When, however, the ligands exert a strong field, the energy of the d_γ orbitals becomes greater than that of the d_ε orbitals, i.e. the d_γ orbitals are destabilised with respect to the d_ε orbitals, and all five electrons occupy the d_ε orbitals since these are of lower energy; in this case, only one electron remains unpaired compared with five when the ligand field acting on the electrons of the iron atom is weak.

Although the ligand field theory has not considered which orbitals are

* To determine the electronic configuration of a transition metal ion, it should be remembered that the s electrons of the neutral atom are ionised off before any d electrons.

used if the bonding between the ligands and the central atom is covalent, it would be expected that sp^3d^2 hybrid orbitals would be used since the arrangement of the ligands is octahedral, and also that d_γ orbitals would more probably be included in the hybridisation than d_ϵ orbitals because of their directional properties. In Fig. 49 the orbitals which can be used to produce the necessary sp^3d^2 hybridisation are indicated.

Since the ligands are regarded as negatively charged in the theory, they are able to provide both electrons for each bond, i.e. the bonds are formally dative covalent bonds, with the ligand atoms acting as donors. If the central Fe^{3+} ion forms six dative bonds it acquires a charge of -3, which is

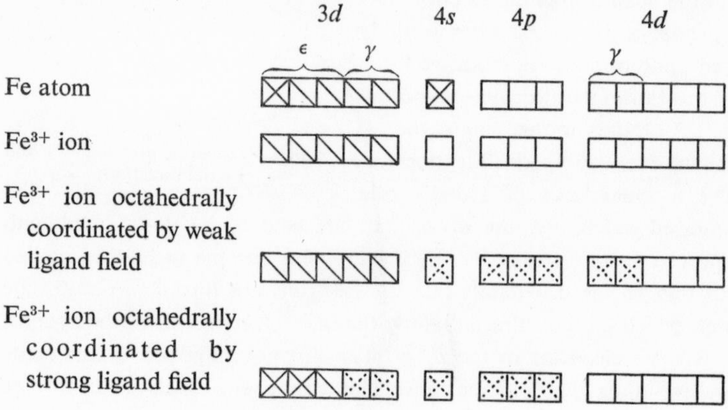

$\searcch$ denotes an electron supplied by a ligand.

FIG. 49

unlikely to be stable since the metal is electropositive. This excess of charge can be lost by means of dative π bonds (p. 105), using available vacant orbitals of the ligand atoms. It can be seen that in the weak field case $4d$ orbitals are required for bond formation since the $3d_\gamma$ orbitals are already occupied by electrons of the iron atom, whereas in the strong field case the $3d$ orbitals can be used for bond formation since the $3d_\gamma$ orbitals are not occupied by electrons of the iron atom. The two hybridisations are differentiated by referring to the former as sp^3d^2 or 'outer' hybrids, and to the latter as d^2sp^3 or 'inner' hybrids.

The two possible configurations for the iron atom in octahedral co-ordination are referred to as spin-free (weak ligand field) and spin-paired (strong ligand field), since in the latter case the electrons are forced to pair off in the d_ϵ orbitals.

The two alternative configurations can be differentiated conveniently by magnetic measurements (see Chapter 2, p. 39), since the iron atom in a spin-free state has a magnetic moment due to five unpaired electrons, whereas in a spin-paired state it is due to one unpaired electron only. An indication of which ligands are likely to exert a strong ligand field is given by the following sequence in which the ligands are arranged in order of increasing field strength:

halogens < water < ammonia and amines < cyanide ion.

Alternatively, the lower the electronegativity of the ligand and the more easily it can be polarised the stronger is the field that it exerts. In accordance with the above sequence, the ion $[Fe^{III}(CN)_6]^{3-}$ is an example of a spin-paired state and the ion $[Fe^{III}F_6]^{3-}$ is an example of a spin-free state.

Almost every element in the d block forms some compounds in which it is octahedrally coordinated, but the octahedral arrangement of the ligands is not always regular; a consideration of the electronic configuration of the central atoms in the various cases is necessary to obtain an understanding of this distortion.

A regular octahedron is highly symmetrical—it has cubic symmetry—and hence octahedral arrangements of atoms can be packed together economically in a crystal lattice,* and this no doubt accounts for the widespread occurrence of this coordination. An octahedral arrangement of ligands is found to be regular if the electrical field due to the non-bonding d electrons of the central atom is also symmetrical, and conversely, if this field due to the non-bonding electrons is not symmetrical it might be expected that the octahedral arrangement of the ligands should be distorted.

Each set of d orbitals is symmetrical when it is completely unoccupied, completely full or is half-full, i.e. has each component orbital singly occupied. Those electronic configurations which are symmetrical are d_γ^0, d_γ^2, d_γ^4 and d_ϵ^0, d_ϵ^3 and d_ϵ^6. The field due to the non-bonding electrons has perfect symmetry only when both the d_γ and the d_ϵ sets are both symmetrical.

In Table XIII are listed the different electronic configurations which are possible for the ion of a d block element when it is at the centre of an octahedral field due to six ligands.

---

* If models are available it can be demonstrated easily that both regular octahedra and tetrahedra can be packed together as closely and economically as can cubes, whereas such polyhedra as trigonal bipyramids, pentagonal bipyramids and even irregular tetrahedra can not.

TABLE XIII

The Sequence in which the d *orbitals of an Atom are filled when it is at the Centre of an Octahedral Ligand Field*

Number of d electrons	Weak ligand field i.e. spin-free		Strong ligand field i.e. spin-paired	
	d_γ	d_ε	d_γ	d_ε
1	0	1 x	0	1 x
2	0	2 x	0	2 x
3	0	3	0	3
4	1	3 xx	0	4 x
5	2	3	0	5 x
6	2	4 x	0	6
7	2	5 x	1	6 xx
8	2	6	2	6 xx
9	3	6 xx	3	6 xx
10	4	6	4	6

It should be noticed that these configurations differ according to whether the ligands exert a strong or a weak field since the former causes spin pairing whereas the latter does not; note also that even when the ligands exert a weak field the d_ε orbitals of the metal atom are occupied before the d_γ orbitals, since an electron in a d_ε orbital is further removed from the repulsive force due to the negatively charged ligands.

Those configurations which give rise to unsymmetrical force fields are indicated in Table XIII by x when the dissymmetry is due to the d_ε orbitals and by xx when it is due to the d_γ orbitals. It is reasonable to assume that the octahedral arrangement of the ligands will be more severely distorted by dissymmetry of the field due to the d_γ orbitals because of the correspondence in direction between the d_γ orbitals of the central atom and the octahedral disposition of the ligands. Such a distortion arising from a dissymmetry of the d_γ orbitals would be expected for the configurations d^9, d^7-spin-paired (i.e. $d_\gamma{}^1 d_\varepsilon{}^6$), and d^4-spin-free (i.e. $d_\gamma{}^1 d_\varepsilon{}^3$), and this has been observed in a large number of cases*. The lesser distortion which would be expected as a result of dissymmetry of the d_ε orbitals has not been observed experimentally, although it may be that more refined techniques will be able to detect it in the future.

A physical picture of how such a distortion arises can be obtained by considering the configuration $d_\gamma{}^1 d_\varepsilon{}^3$ as an example. The single electron

* See below, p. 115, for the configuration d^8.

in the d_γ orbitals occupies the d_{z^2} orbital so that when the ligands approach the central atom they can approach more closely along the directions of the x and y axes, since they are not repelled by the presence of any electrons in the $d_{x^2-y^2}$ orbital, than along the direction of the z axis because of the electron in the d_{z^2} orbital. The octahedral arrangement is thus distorted in such a way that two diametrically opposite ligands, i.e. those which approach along the direction of the z axis, remain at a greater distance from the central atom than do the other four; i.e. the central atom can be regarded as forming two long and four short bonds with the surrounding atoms. Similar reasoning can be applied to the configurations d^7 and d^9. Note that a distortion of the octahedral arrangement of ligands is caused by a metal ion with the configuration d^4 when the ligands exert a weak ligand field, e.g. halogen atoms, but by a metal ion with the configuration d^7 when the ligands exert a strong ligand field, e.g. cyanide ions; when the metal ion has the configuration d^9, a distortion is caused whether the ligands exert a strong or a weak ligand field.

When the electronic configuration d^8 is acted upon by an octahedral ligand field it becomes $d_\epsilon^6 d_\gamma^2$ no matter whether the ligands exert a strong or a weak field (Table XIII). However, if the ligand field is strong it can cause spin-pairing within the d_γ orbitals so that both electrons occupy the d_{z^2} orbital, and the $d_{x^2-y^2}$ orbital is unoccupied. The repulsion of the ligands by the electrons in the d_{z^2} orbital is then sufficiently great to make even a distorted octahedral arrangement of six ligands impossible and a square planar arrangement of four ligands results; in this arrangement two ligands are regarded as having been repelled to infinity as a result of the repulsion by the electrons in the d_{z^2} orbital. d^8 is the electronic configuration of nickel(II) and its congeners, and also of gold(III), and it is found that several compounds of nickel(II), etc., have square planar structures. The configuration d^8 can still have a regular octahedral coordination, however, if the ligands exert only a weak field.

Tetrahedral Ligand Field

When four ligands approach the central atom tetrahedrally, the directions of their approach do not coincide exactly with either the d_γ or the d_ϵ orbitals of the central atom, but they correspond appreciably more closely with the d_ϵ than with the d_γ set. To show this, consider Fig. 50. This represents a cube at the centre of which is the nucleus of the atom. The d_γ orbitals are concentrated along three directions at right angles to each other and these pass through the face centres of the cube. The maximum probability distributions of the d_ϵ orbitals lie intermediate between those of the d_γ orbitals and are directed from the nucleus towards the mid-points of the cube edges (only one shown in the Figure). Four ligands occupy alternate corners of the cube and thus constitute a tetrahedral arrangement round the central nucleus. It can be shown that a line drawn through the position occupied by a ligand to the nucleus makes an angle of 35° 16′ with the direction of a d_ϵ orbital and of 54° 44′ with the direction of a d_γ orbital. As a consequence of this, the picture for tetrahedral ligands is the inverse of that described for octahedral ligands.

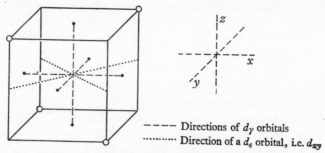

———— Directions of d_γ orbitals

············ Direction of a d_ϵ orbital, i.e. d_{xy}

FIG. 50 The relationship between a regular tetrahedron and the x, y and z axial directions.

In Table XIV are listed the different electronic configurations possible for the ion of a d block element when it is at the centre of a tetrahedral field due to four ligands. Once again the configurations differ according to whether the ligands exert a strong or a weak ligand field.

Even a strong tetrahedral ligand field does not produce such a large difference between the energy levels of the d_γ and the d_ϵ orbitals as does a strong octahedral field, and in consequence spin pairing is much less important when considering tetrahedral ligands. Nevertheless, the configurations for both spin-free and spin-paired states are given in Table XIV. Also in contrast to the case of the octahedral field, the d_γ orbitals of the central atom are occupied in preference to the d_ϵ orbitals, as can be seen by comparing Tables XIII and XIV, since the d_ϵ orbitals of the central atom are more nearly coincident in direction with that of the approaching tetrahedral ligands.

A regular tetrahedral group of ligands, like an octahedral group, has cubic symmetry, and distortion of the tetrahedral arrangement would be expected when there is dissymmetry of the non-bonding electrons. Those configurations are marked xx in Table XIV which have dissymmetry due to an unsymmetrical occupancy of the d_ϵ orbitals, and x which have dissymmetry due to the d_γ orbitals. It is clear that dissymmetry due to the d_ε orbitals is more likely to produce a distortion of a regular tetrahedral arrangement than that due to d_γ orbitals, just as the converse was seen to be true for octahedral arrangements. Tetrahedral coordination is apparently less stable (or less energetically favourable) than octahedral coordination so that not only those configurations marked xx (i.e. d_ε orbitals unsymmetrically occupied) but also those marked x (i.e. d_γ orbitals unsymmetrically occupied) rarely, if ever, occur in tetrahedral coordination.* It will be seen below that tetrahedral coordination is known for compounds in which the central atom has one of the following configurations: d^0, d^1, d^2, d^5, d^7 or d^{10} and reference to Table XIV shows that of these possibilities only d^1 might be expected to be distorted, or even too unstable to exist.

TABLE XIV

The Sequence in which the d orbitals of an Atom are occupied when it is at the Centre of a Tetrahedral Ligand Field

Number of d electrons	Weak ligand field i.e. spin-free		Strong ligand field i.e. spin-paired	
	d_γ	d_ε	d_γ	d_ε
1	1	0 x	1	0 x
2	2	0	2	0
3	2	1 xx	3	0 x
4	2	2 xx	4	0
5	2	3	4	1 xx
6	3	3 x	4	2 xx
7	4	3	4	3
8	4	4 xx	4	4 xx
9	4	5 xx	4	5 xx
10	4	6	4	6

Some Properties of Transition Elements

Before the applications of the ligand field theory are considered in a discussion of various examples, it may be of advantage to outline some of the characteristic features of the transition elements as a whole. Firstly, as a result of their lower abundance in Nature, there is not the same detailed knowledge about the chemistry of many of the transition elements,

* See, however, p. 123.

and in particular about the structure of their compounds, as there is about some of the more common s and p block elements such as, for example, sodium, oxygen and the halogens; this is particularly true of the second- and third-row transition elements, although it must be added that this deficiency of knowledge is rapidly being overcome. Most of the examples of structures which are referred to below are of compounds of elements which are in the first row of the transition series, i.e. scandium—zinc.

Secondly, because of the greater polarising power of the transition metal ions, complexes are much more numerous than simple compounds, and this also is reflected in the examples to be considered.

Thirdly, each element can exist in a number of different oxidation states and it is not always easy to predict which oxidation state(s) will be most stable for any element; for example, if element A reacts with fluorine, the formula of the product (which depends upon the oxidation state of A) cannot always be predicted with certainty, as it could be for most of the main group elements, e.g. calcium, boron, etc.

Finally, it should be noted that the d block elements form molecules and ions which have different shapes from those described in the previous chapter for main-group elements, notably the square planar arrangement for a coordination number of four and the face-centred octahedral arrangement for a coordination number of seven.

The Structure of Compounds of the Transition Elements

In the following pages a number of molecules and ions will be discussed from a structural point of view. It is suggested that the following sequence of steps should be adopted in attempting to deduce the structure of a molecule or ion which has a transition metal as the central atom:

(1) Write down the electronic configuration of the appropriate transition element in its ground state.

(2) Determine the oxidation state of the element in the compound under consideration (see footnote on p. 6) and by subtracting the appropriate number of electrons (see footnote on p. 111) from the configuration given in (1) obtain the configuration of the ion in this particular oxidation state. Note that although this procedure is adopted, there is no suggestion that this is the mechanism employed by the element in forming a compound, or that the compound is purely ionic.

(3) Count the number of atoms which surround the central atom and can be assumed to have some degree of covalent bonding to it and

select orbitals in the order s, p and d* so that there is one orbital for each bonded atom (since each orbital can contain a pair of electrons). Consider these orbitals to be hybridised, and determine the stereochemistry which corresponds to this hybridisation by reference to Table XII, p. 101.

(4) Consider the possible effect of a ligand field in producing spin pairing, and the possible distortion that may be caused by non-bonding electrons which occupy orbitals which are not used in the hybridisation.

The structures of a number of molecules and ions will now be considered in detail to illustrate how the above procedure can be used, although a warning should be given at the outset that there are difficulties in some cases which are not easily resolved.

(1) Molecules and Ions with a Coordination Number of 2

In most of the known examples of molecules and ions with a coordination number of two, the configuration of the central ion, i.e. the atom in its appropriate oxidation state, is either d^0 or d^{10}.

(i) The vanadyl ion, VO_2^+

The electronic configuration of vanadium is s^2d^3, and in the vanadyl ion the vanadium atom is in an oxidation state of $+5$.

$$[V(+5)+2\ O(-2)=\text{residual charge of } +1.]$$

When five electrons are removed from the vanadium atom to give vanadium(V), its configuration becomes s^0d^0, and since two oxygen atoms are bonded to the vanadium atom, two orbitals are required. The first two available (in accordance with (3) above) are an s and a p orbital, and these are hybridised to give two sp hybrid orbitals so that a linear arrangement of atoms is found in the structure of the ion. As there are no d electrons in the vanadium(V), no distortion of the linear arrangement is likely. The uranyl ion, UO_2^{2+}, in which the uranium atom has an oxidation state of $+6$ and the electronic configuration d^0, is also known to be linear, as is the uranol ion, UO_2^+, in which the uranium atom has an oxidation state of $+5$ and the configuration d^1 (or perhaps f^1?). Presumably the one non-bonding electron in the case of the uranol ion can occupy an orbital where it is unable to cause any distortion of the

---

* This does not imply that the $4p$ level is of lower energy than the $3d$, etc., but is used only as a convenient approach.

linear arrangement, e.g. in the d_{z^2} orbital, which is perpendicular to the sp hybrid orbitals.

(ii) The ion [Ag(CN)₂]⁻

The electronic configuration of silver might have been expected to be s^2d^9, but it appears that the alternative s^1d^{10}, which would be expected to be of very similar energy, represents the ground state of the silver atom. Presumably the stability of a complete d level influences this. In the above ion the silver atom is in an oxidation state of $+1$, and the removal of one electron leaves the configuration s^0d^{10}; hence, as in the case of the vanadyl ion, sp hybridisation of the orbitals of the silver atom results so that a linear arrangement of bonds from the silver to the carbon atoms is found; since the configuration d^{10} is symmetrical, no distortion is to be expected. (When a cyanide ion is covalently bonded to a metal atom, as in this complex ion, the carbon atom forms two σ bonds, one to the nitrogen atom and the other to the metal atom, and two π bonds both to the nitrogen atom; i.e. it is written as :N≡C—Ag—C≡N:. Hence the bonds from the carbon atoms use sp hybrid orbitals and are linear, and since the bonds from the silver atom also use linear hybrid orbitals, it follows that in the ion [Ag(CN)₂]⁻ all four bonds, and hence all five atoms, are collinear.)

Other examples of molecules and ions in which the bonds from the central atom are linear, and the central atom also has the configuration d^{10} include $HgCl_2$, $Zn(CH_3)_2$, $[Ag(NH_3)_2]^+$, $[Cu^I(CN)_2]^-$, $[AuCl_2]^-$, etc.

(2) Molecules and Ions with a Coordination Number of 3

These are rare, but a planar arrangement of atoms around a central atom using sp^2 hybrid orbitals would be expected unless it was distorted by the non-bonding electrons.

(3) Molecules and Ions with a Coordination Number of 4

As was pointed out in the discussion of the Ligand Field Theory, there are two possible arrangements of atoms which correspond to a coordination number of four. These are (i) tetrahedral, which is the distribution of sp^3 hybrid orbitals, and (ii) square planar, which is the distribution of sp^2d hybrid orbitals. This latter type of hybridisation would not be anticipated in accordance with the third step of the procedure outlined on p. 118, since the order of choosing orbitals given there leads to one s and three p orbitals being used before any d orbitals. However, the ligand field theory affords a satisfactory approach to an understanding of four-fold coordination.

(i) Titanium Tetrachloride, $TiCl_4$

The electronic configuration of titanium is s^2d^2 and in the tetrachloride the titanium atom is in an oxidation state of $+4$. Removal of four electrons produces the configuration s^0d^0, and the first four available orbitals are one s and three p, so that sp^3 hybrid orbitals of the titanium atom are used and a tetrahedral structure for the molecule results. As there is no dissymmetry associated with the configuration d^0, the molecule is undistorted. Other examples of tetrahedral structures in which the central atom has the configuration d^0 are the isoelectronic series of ions VO_4^{3-}, CrO_4^{2-} and MnO_4^-, in which the metal atoms are in the oxidation states of $+5$, $+6$ and $+7$ respectively.

Certain elements in the two groups which follow the titanium group, e.g. vanadium and molybdenum, also form tetrahalides. Whereas titanium(IV) has the configuration d^0, that of vanadium(IV) is d^1 and that of molybdenum(IV) is d^2. A tetrahedral structure would be expected for these tetrahalides just as for titanium tetrachloride; in accordance with the previous argument (see Table XIV), a slight distortion of the tetrahedral structure might be expected for the configuration d^1, although this distortion has not been observed in the structure of vanadium tetrachloride. A regular tetrahedral structure would be expected, however, for compounds in which the central atom has the configuration d^2, and this has been observed in the structure of the ion FeO_4^{2-}, in which the iron atom is in the oxidation state of $+6$.

It appears that very few, if any, molecules or ions are known to have a tetrahedral structure in which the central atom has a configuration of d^3, d^4 or d^6. Considering only the more important spin-free state, it can be seen from Table XIV that a gross distortion of the tetrahedral arrangement is to be expected for the configurations d^3 and d^4 and a lesser distortion for d^6, so that it is likely that such compounds are too unstable to be formed. Undistorted tetrahedral structures are to be expected, however, for molecules and ions in which the transition metal has the electronic configuration d^5, d^7 or d^{10}.

(ii) The ion $FeCl_4^-$

The electronic configuration of an iron atom is s^2d^6 and in the $FeCl_4^-$ ion the iron is in the oxidation state of $+3$. Removal of three electrons

I

produces the configuration s^0d^5 and the first four orbitals available are again one s and three p, so that sp^3 hybrid orbitals of the iron atom are used and the ion has a tetrahedral structure which is not distorted since the configuration of the non-bonding electrons, i.e. d^5, is symmetrical.

(iii) The ion $CoCl_4{}^{2-}$

An exactly similar discussion can be applied to this ion since cobalt(II) has the symmetrical configuration d^7.

(iv) The ion $[Zn(NH_3)_4]^{2+}$

A larger number of compounds with tetrahedral structures is known when the transition metal has the configuration d^{10} than for any other configuration. The factor which contributes largely to this is that a metal atom in such a compound gains an inert gas type of configuration. This can be seen by considering as an example the ion $[Zn(NH_3)_4]^{2+}$. A zinc atom has the configuration s^2d^{10} and in the oxidation state of $+2$ this becomes s^0d^{10}. Each ammonia molecule, by forming a dative covalent bond with the nitrogen atom as the donor, donates two electrons to the zinc atom, and these eight electrons fill the four sp^3 hybrid orbitals of the zinc atom, so that it then has the configuration $s^2d^{10}p^6$, which is that of the inert gas krypton.

Tetrahedral structures in which the metal atom has the configuration d^{10} are found in compounds of zinc(II), cadmium(II), and mercury(II), copper(I), silver(I) and gold(I), and nickel(0); e.g. $[Cu(CN)_4]^{3-}$, $[HgI_4]^{2-}$ and $Ni(CO)_4$.

Those configurations for which four-fold coordination have not been considered so far are d^8 and d^9. In both cases tetrahedral arrangements would be expected to be grossly distorted (Table XIV) and they are presumably too unstable to exist. It was seen, however, in the discussion of octahedral ligand fields (p. 115), that an octahedral distribution of ligands would be considerably distorted around metal atoms which have the configurations d^8 (d_γ spin-paired) and d^9, and that the distortion would be such that two diametrically opposite ligands are situated further from the central atom than the other four which are disposed towards the corners of a square. If these two ligands are removed completely, the central atom is in a position of four-fold coordination with a square planar distribution. It was also pointed out on p. 115 that the removal of the two ligands is complete when the central atom has the configuration d^8 (spin-paired) but it is incomplete when that configuration is d^9.

The configuration d^8 is that of nickel(II) and its congeners, and a large number of compounds of these elements have a square planar structure, e.g. nickel dimethyl glyoxime (see Fig. 51), $[Ni(CN)_4]^{2-}$, $[PdCl_4]^{2-}$, etc. This stereochemistry requires that the transition metal atom should use sp^2d hybrid orbitals if there is any degree of covalent bonding with the ligand atoms (it should be noted that the $d_{x^2-y^2}$ orbital is unoccupied in the d^8 spin-paired configuration, and this can be combined with an s and the p_x and p_y orbitals to make four vacant hybrid orbitals in the xy plane), and it was pointed out on p. 120 that the third step in the procedure of p. 118 must be modified in the light of the ligand field theory in order to give an understanding of this particular stereochemistry.

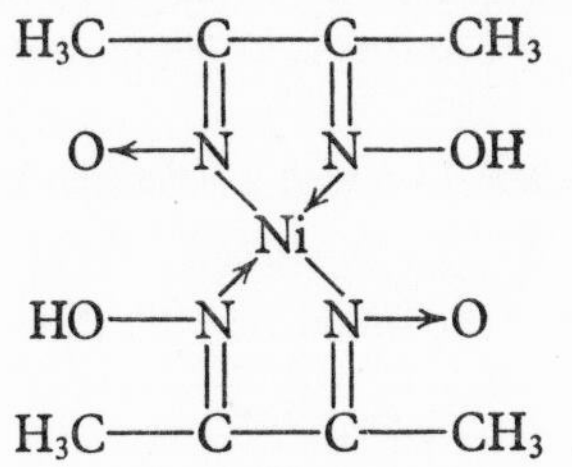

$$\begin{array}{c}
\text{H}_3\text{C}\text{---}\text{C}\text{---}\text{C}\text{---}\text{CH}_3 \\
\text{O}\leftarrow\text{N} \quad \text{N}\text{---}\text{OH} \\
\text{Ni} \\
\text{HO}\text{---}\text{N} \quad \text{N}\rightarrow\text{O} \\
\text{H}_3\text{C}\text{---}\text{C}\text{---}\text{C}\text{---}\text{CH}_3
\end{array}$$

FIG. 51 The molecule of nickel dimethyl glyoxime.

It was believed earlier that a large number of compounds of nickel(II) has a tetrahedral structure, but it has recently been established that this belief was based upon a wrong interpretation of the experimental evidence. Some examples in which nickel(II) has a tetrahedral structure are now known with certainty, but in some of these cases this structure can be regarded as being forced upon the nickel atom by steric considerations, e.g. nickel occupies tetrahedral sites in the ionic lattice of nickel chromite, $NiCr_2O_4$, which is a spinel (Chapter 3, p. 72), and the only sites of four-fold coordination in the spinel lattice are tetrahedral ones. The tetrahedral arrangement of oxygen atoms around the nickel atom is distorted as expected—see Table XIV; and in consequence the unit cell of the spinel is no longer a perfect cube. Similar distortions are also found when Mn(III) and Cu(II) occupy octahedral sites in spinels.

Four-coordinate nickel(II) is thus a common coordination and it is usually square planar and not tetrahedral. Nickel(II) can also be octahedrally coordinated, as for example in the ion $[Ni(H_2O)_6]^{2+}$. This is a quite straightforward case and a regular octahedral coordination would be expected for the spin-free state (see Table XIII).

The configuration d^9 is that of copper(II) (silver(II) and gold(II) are uncommon oxidation states of these elements), and molecules and ions are known in which the copper atom appears to have a coordination number of four, e.g. $[Cu(NH_3)_4]^{2+}$ and $[Cu(CN)_4]^{2-}$. Whereas the copper atom is surrounded by a square planar arrangement of ligands in these ions and in other molecules also, the crystal lattice in most, if not all, cases is such that it has two slightly more distant neighbours (which belong to the square configurations around other copper atoms) which make up the arrangement of a distorted octahedron, as is to be expected from the above arguments.

It is thus more accurate to describe copper(II) as being six-coordinate in its compounds, with the reservation that the octahedral arrangement is always distorted, than to describe it as being four-coordinate.

(4) Molecules and Ions with a Coordination Number of 5

This is another relatively uncommon coordination number for d block elements as it was seen to be for s and p block elements, presumably for the same reason.

Vanadium pentafluoride, VF_5

The electronic configuration of a vanadium atom is s^2d^3, and in the oxidation state of $+5$ this becomes s^0d^0. In accordance with the sequence outlined on p. 118 the first five available orbitals of the vanadium(V) atom are one s, three p and one d, so that sp^3d hybrid orbitals are used and in consequence the molecule has a trigonal bipyramidal structure (Table XII, p. 101). Other molecules for which this structure has been found include NbF_5 and TaF_5, both niobium(V) and tantalum(V) having the configuration d^0 also.

Some compounds are known in which the atoms are arranged in the shape of a square-based pyramid (Fig. 42), e.g. $NiBr_3 . 2P(C_2H_5)_3$, but knowledge concerning five-fold coordination is less complete.

(5) Molecules and Ions with a Coordination Number of 6

Almost every transition element forms some compounds in which its atom is surrounded by six other atoms to which it is bonded covalently; most frequently these compounds contain the transition element in a complex ion. The arrangement of the six atoms is almost invariably octahedral although there are some exceptions such as the trigonal prismatic arrangement of sulphur atoms around a molybdenum atom in the structure of molybdenum disulphide. As was seen in the discussion of the application of the ligand field theory to six-fold coordination (p. 110), octahedral arrangements are almost invariably regular, so that only the exceptions to this need be considered here. The configurations for which distorted octahedral arrangements are to be expected are d^4 (spin-free) and d^9, Table XIII. Those compounds of chromium(II) and manganese(III), which have the configuration d^4, and of copper(II), d^9, in which the metal has been found to be octahedrally coordinated, show that the octahedral arrangements are distorted as expected. Some such compounds of copper(II) were quoted above. Perhaps better known examples are compounds which have lattices of appreciably ionic character, e.g. CrF_2, MnF_3 and CuO, and these will be considered further in the following chapter. Ligand field theory regards compounds from an ionic point of view, but its predictions are found to be valid for both ionic and covalent compounds.

(6) Molecules and Ions with a Coordination Number > 6

Molecules and ions in which the central metal atom has a coordination number greater than six are not very numerous and it will suffice to describe a few examples without attempting a more comprehensive treatment.

The ion ZrF_7^{3-} has a pentagonal bipyramidal arrangement of fluorine atoms around a central zirconium atom, cf. IF_7, whereas the isoelectronic ion TaF_7^{2-} appears, somewhat surprisingly, to have a different structure in which six of the fluorine atoms are at the corners of a trigonal prism and the remaining one is at the centre of one of the faces, as shown in Fig. 52.

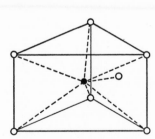

FIG. 52 A face-centred trigonal prism—structure of the ion TaF_7^{2-}.

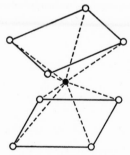

FIG. 53 A square antiprism —structure of the ion TaF_8^{3-}.

In the ion TaF_8^{3-}, the fluorine atoms lie at the corners of a square antiprism, Fig 53; i.e. a cube of which the top is skewed through an angle of 45° with respect to the base. In contrast to this structure, the cyanide groups in the ion $[Mo(CN)_8]^{4-}$ occupy the corners of a dodecahedron, Fig. 54. The hatched circles lie at the corners of one tetrahedron, and the open circles at the corners of a second tetrahedron, both tetrahedra having a common centre. Each corner of the second etrahedron lies on a line from the body-centre to a face-centre of the first tetrahedron, but projected beyond that face. An example of nine-fold coordination is afforded by the ion $[Nd(H_2O)_9]^{3+}$ in which the water molecules are sited at the corners and the face-centres of a trigonal prism.

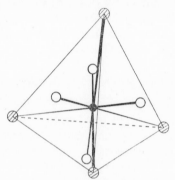

Fig. 54 The apices of a dodecahedron—structure of $[Mo(CN)_8]^{4-}$.

7

THE STRUCTURES OF COVALENT
COMPOUNDS—PART III

Polynuclear Molecules and Ions and Three-dimensional Covalent Structures

In the two preceding chapters the compounds considered contained bonds of predominantly covalent character, and their crystal structures were built of discrete simple molecules and ions. The stereochemistry of the whole molecule or ion could be deduced by considering one atom only, because each other atom formed only one covalent bond.

There are many substances in which the bonding is appreciably covalent but whose structures were not considered in Chapters 5 or 6, either because their constituent molecules or ions contain more than one atom whose stereochemistry must be considered, or because no discrete molecules or ions can be detected in these structures. In a sense, these structures can be regarded as being formed by the 'polymerisation' of a simple unit.

These structures will now be described in this chapter under the heading of 'polymers', and will be divided for convenience into four categories:

(1) The non-metallic elements.
(2) Covalent three-dimensional lattices such as that of zinc blende.
(3) Finite, polynuclear molecules such as P_4O_{10}, etc.
(4) Poly-anions.

(1) The Structures of the non-metallic Elements

Whereas the structures of the metallic elements can be regarded as the packing together of spherical atoms as economically as possible and with no localisation of electrons in particular orientations in space, the atoms of the non-metallic elements are bonded to each other by covalent bonds so that the environment of each atom is governed by the orbitals which are available for bonding.

The inert gases are exceptional in that they form no covalent bonds, so that their structures can be compared with those of the metals, and are based on close-packing (Chapter 3, p. 44). The other non-metallic elements are found in groups IV-VII of the Periodic Table. The number of the group corresponds with the number of electrons which an atom of an element in that group has in its s and p levels together, and, representing the group number as N, the number of electrons which an atom must gain to reach the configuration of the nearest inert gas (which has eight electrons in its s and p levels) is $8 - N$. This number of electrons is gained by forming $(8 - N)$ σ covalent bonds so that $(8 - N)$ represents the number of neighbouring bonded atoms or the coordination number to be expected for an atom of the element in the crystal. Each atom by forming $(8 - N)$ bonds acquires an octet of electrons in its valency shell and the octet is 1, 2, 3 or 4 covalent according to whether the element is in group VII, VI, V or IV respectively; the stereochemistry of the element is in accord with the valency group of each atom. Each group will be considered in turn.

The elements of group VII, the halogens, have a coordination number of one and form diatomic molecules. The elements of group VI, with the exception of the diatomic molecule of oxygen, have a coordination number of two and their atoms have as a valency group a di-covalent octet, so that a bond angle of $\leqslant 109°$ is to be expected. When each individual atom is bonded to two other identical atoms, there are two possible structural arrangements; either an infinite chain can be formed or the chain can 'bite its own tail' and become a ring, thus becoming a molecule of finite size instead of being infinite. Both these arrangements are found; thus sulphur and selenium can form cyclic molecules S_8 and Se_8 which are puckered, with a bond angle of approximately 105°, and not planar rings since the latter would require too large a bond angle, i.e. 135°; plastic sulphur, grey selenium and tellurium form infinite chains.

The elements of group V, with the exception of the diatomic molecule of nitrogen, have a coordination number of three and their atoms have as a valency group a three-covalent octet, so that a pyramidal arrangement of bonds is to be expected (cf. the ammonia molecule, p. 97). As in group VI, the elements in this group are polymorphic. However, phosphorus, arsenic and antimony, like sulphur and selenium, can exist in one form as discrete molecules; these molecules are tetratomic, each atom being at the corner of a regular tetrahedron and thus having a coordination number of three. (Note that there is no atom at the centre of the tetrahedron.) The bond angle in this structure is 60°, which is very different from the expected angle of approximately 105°; this imposes such a strain that none of these molecules is stable at normal temperatures. All the elements in the group exist also in more metallic forms; the structure adopted by arsenic, antimony and bismuth is three-dimensional and contains no discrete molecules. It can best be described by reference to the structure of sodium chloride. Imagine that all the atoms in that lattice are of the same element, so that each atom has six nearest neighbours arranged octahedrally; the lattice is then distorted so that, for any one octahedron, three of the neighbouring atoms become appreciably further distant than the other three, and three nearer neighbours make a pyramidal arrangement since they all lie on the one side of the atom which was at the centre of the originally regular octahedron. The distortion also causes the bond angle to exceed the 90° of a regular octahedron; in the ammonia molecule, which also has a three-covalent octet as the valency group of the nitrogen atom, the bond angle is 107°.

The elements of group IV have a coordination number of four and their atoms have as a valency group a four-covalent octet, so that a structure in which each atom is surrounded tetrahedrally is to be expected. No discrete molecules are found for these elements and each, except the most metallic member of the group—lead, which has a close-packed structure, can have a three-dimensional lattice with tetrahedral coordination. This structure is identical with that of zinc blende (Chapter 3, p. 55) except that all the atoms are of the same element. The modification of carbon which has this structure is diamond; the hardness of diamond can be attributed to the strength (large bond energy) of the carbon—carbon bond and to there being no particular direction through the crystal in which cleavage can occur without having to break a great many of those bonds.

Both carbon and tin are dimorphic. The second form of tin, white tin, can be regarded as having the same lattice, although it is severely distorted. The second modification of carbon, graphite, has a completely different structure with a coordination number of three instead of four. As was seen in Chapter 5, p. 108, the carbon atoms use sp^2 hybrid orbitals and are arranged in planar sheets with interbond angles of 120°; the sheets of atoms stack themselves one on top of the other with a distance between the sheets of 3·35 Å compared with a distance of 1·42 Å between adjacent atoms in a sheet. The force of attraction between the sheets is relatively weak and hence graphite can be cleaved into flakes and accordingly is used sometimes as a lubricant.

A direct result of the structure of graphite is its ability to form intercalation compounds in which atoms and molecules are pushed between the layers of carbon atoms, and bonding is made possible because of the availability of the π electrons of the graphite. An example of such a compound is carbon monofluoride, CF, in which presumably each carbon atom forms a σ bond to a fluorine atom in addition to the three by which it is already bonded to neighbouring carbon atoms. By forming this bond, each carbon becomes four covalent so that a tetrahedral structure should result leading to a buckling of the sheets.

It was pointed out in Chapter 5, p. 107, that graphite and boron nitride were isostructural, and in accordance with this the planar modification of boron nitride can also form intercalation compounds.

(2) Three-dimensional Covalent Lattices

In Chapter 3 a number of lattices of binary compounds were described which have features usually associated with ionic lattices. These lattices were seen to be infinite in three dimensions and to contain no discrete molecules; an atom of the one kind is surrounded by atoms of the other kind, and the ratio of the coordination numbers of the atoms of the two different elements corresponds to the stoichiometry of the compound. However, it was pointed out in Chapter 4 that the coordination numbers cannot be predicted by means of radius ratio considerations, as is possible for ionic compounds, and that the compounds which adopt these lattices possess an appreciable amount of covalent character. Some further consideration can now be given to these structures.

The most important of these lattices are those of zinc blende, wurtzite and nickel arsenide for compounds of type AB and cadmium iodide, cadmium chloride and pyrites for compounds of type AB_2. In the following discussion no attempt will be made to differentiate between the lattices of zinc blende and wurtzite, cadmium iodide and cadmium chloride, or pyrites and marcasite, etc., on account of their similarities (see Chapter 3).

When the compounds which have these various structures are listed, it is apparent that the metal is most often a d block element; accordingly the concept of radius ratio which was used as an approach to an understanding of ionic lattices can be replaced by the ligand field theory. The electronegative element in the compounds is usually a member of group VI or VII of the Periodic Table (omitting oxygen and fluorine since oxides and fluorides usually have ionic lattices), so that the metal is in an oxidation state of $+1$ or $+2$, or less frequently $+4$. (Compounds formed between the transition metals and the non-metallic elements of group V are sometimes interstitial in character, but many of them can also be included here.)

The structures of compounds of type AB will be considered first. The ligand field theory was used in Chapter 6 to explain the stability of octahedral coordination, and showed which electronic configurations give rise to stable tetrahedral, square planar and distorted octahedral coordination.

These coordinations are found in covalent three-dimensional lattices as well as in discrete molecules and ions.

An atom of a metallic element is likely to be surrounded by four atoms of a non-metallic element in tetrahedral coordination only if it has an electronic configuration of d^0, d^2, d^5, d^7 or d^{10} (Table XIV) and in each case regular octahedral coordination is also stable. An oxidation state of $+1$ or $+2$ coupled with a configuration of either d^0 or d^2 is not possible for any transition metal with the exception of titanium(II) which is very unstable. The only possible example of the configuration d^5, discounting technetium and rhenium which do not commonly form compounds in an oxidation state of $+2$, is manganese(II), and the polymorphic manganese sulphide and selenide (as also the oxide) can have the tetrahedral zinc blende and wurtzite structures as well as the octahedral sodium chloride structure. Manganese telluride and arsenide, which are still more covalent in character, adopt the more covalent structure of nickel arsenide.

The configuration d^7 is represented by cobalt(II), but none of its compounds is known to have a tetrahedral zinc blende or wurtzite structure.

The configuration d^{10} is found in copper(I) and zinc(II) and their congeners, and as was pointed out on p. 122, there is the added feature which applies to no other configuration that when elements of this configuration form four covalent bonds they reach the electronic configuration of the nearest inert gas; this no doubt accounts for the preference of four rather than six coordination which the elements with this configuration show, since six-fold coordination is also stable. The halides of copper(I) and silver iodide (but surprisingly not silver chloride and silver bromide) and the oxides, sulphides, etc., of zinc(II), cadmium(II) and mercury(II) have the zinc blende and wurtzite structures.

Other compounds which adopt these structures are those formed by gallium(III) and indium(III) with the group V elements, (although these metals are not d block elements, gallium(III) and indium(III) are isoelectronic with zinc(II) and cadmium(II) respectively so that it is not surprising that they should form compounds with the same structure); also, compounds of aluminium(III) (aluminium being a congener of gallium and indium) and the isoelectronic beryllium(II) with group V and VI elements respectively.

An atom of a metallic element is likely to be surrounded by four atoms of a non-metallic element arranged in a square-plane arrangement if the metal has the configuration d^8, and by six atoms of a non-metallic element arranged in a distorted octahedral arrangement if the metal has the configuration d^4 or d^9. There are a number of binary compounds known which have structures in which the metal atom has these coordinations and these structures were not described in Chapter 3 since they are somewhat special cases. These structures possess the unusual feature, compared with those described previously, in that the non-metallic atom is surrounded by four metal atoms arranged tetrahedrally, as would be expected since these atoms have a four-covalent octet as their valency group. These compounds are binary compounds of platinum(II) and palladium(II), of configuration d^8, and copper(II), of configuration d^9; not only the sulphides, etc., of

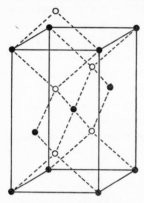

FIG. 55 The structure of platinum(II) oxide.

these elements in the +2 oxidation state, but also the oxides have structures of this type, and as an example (since they are not identical in detail although similar in principle) the lattice of platinum(II) oxide, PtO, is shown in Fig. 55.

Note that nickel(II) compounds which have three-dimensional covalent lattices do not have a square-planar arrangement around the nickel atom as might have been expected since nickel(II) has the electronic configuration d^8; this might be due to the appropriate non-metallic elements exerting a ligand field which is not sufficiently strong to bring about the spin-pairing which is required before nickel can adopt a square-planar arrangement (p. 115). It has also been pointed out previously that nickel(II) can be octahedrally coordinated (p. 123).

With the exception of the compounds which have been considered above in whose structures the metal atom has four-fold coordination (or distorted six-fold, as in the case of copper(II)), regular octahedral coordination is to be expected and is found in the numerous compounds which adopt the nickel arsenide structure. No halides are known to have this structure; the only metals which can show an oxidation state of +1 and thus form halides of the formula AB, i.e. copper, silver and gold, were seen above to have tetrahedral coordination, i.e. their halides usually adopt the zinc blende and wurtzite lattices.

Compounds which adopt the nickel arsenide structure are very numerous and include:

(a) compounds of vanadium(II) (d^3), chromium(II) (d^4), manganese(II) (d^5), iron(II) (d^6), cobalt(II) (d^7), and nickel(II) (d^8) with sulphur, selenium and tellurium;

(b) compounds of chromium(III) (d^3), manganese(III) (d^4), iron(III) (d^5), cobalt(III) (d^6) and nickel(III) (d^7) with arsenic and antimony.

The electronic configurations which are missing from this list are: (i) d^0, d^1 and d^2 because there are no corresponding metal ions with a charge of $+1$ or $+2$. (ii) d^9 because it requires a distorted octahedral coordination (see Cu(II) above). (iii) d^{10} because the metals prefer tetrahedral coordination, as was pointed out above. The inclusion of d^4 is a little surprising, but regular octahedral coordination is stable for this configuration when it is spin paired, unlike the case of d^9. It has also been indicated that the configuration d^8 can have both square planar or octahedral coordination.

To summarise, if the compound AB is not sufficiently ionic to adopt the sodium chloride (or caesium chloride) structure, the metal is likely to have tetrahedral coordination if its electronic configuration is d^{10}, i.e. the compound is likely to have the zinc blende or wurtzite structure; the metal is likely to have a distorted octahedral coordination if its configuration is d^9, i.e. the compound is not likely to have one of the structures described in Chapter 3; if the configuration of the metal is d^8, its coordination might be square planar or octahedral, i.e. the compound might have a unique structure, or the nickel arsenide structure—compounds of nickel(II) prefer the latter, whereas compounds of platinum(II) and palladium(II) prefer the former; if the metal has a configuration $d \leqslant 7$ it is likely to have a regular octahedral coordination, and the compound the nickel arsenide structure. (Remember that ligand field theory regards metals as being positive ions so that all the above configurations refer to ions, even although the compounds are appreciably covalent in character.)

For compounds of type AB_2, there is not the same choice of possible coordinations. The only structures in which an atom of element A is surrounded tetrahedrally are those of the different modifications of silicon dioxide (see β-cristobalite, Chapter 3, p. 62), and no compounds of metallic elements, not even those with the configuration d^{10}, are known which adopt this type of structure. The halides of copper(II), palladium(II) and platinum(II) have structures in which the metal again has a square planar coordination (copper also having the two extra neighbours to give it a distorted octahedral arrangement), but apart from these exceptions regular six-fold coordination is the rule. When atom B is a halogen other than fluorine, the compound has a cadmium halide structure; if atom B is one of the less electronegative elements of group VI, the structure adopted is usually that of pyrites or marcasite, and in these lattices the metal appears always to be in an oxidation state of $+2$, i.e. the anion is S_2^{2-}, etc. A few cases are known of sulphides, selenides and tellurides which adopt a cadmium halide structure, but these metals are, in contrast to the metals in the pyrites and marcasite lattices, in an oxidation state of $+4$ and the anion is S^{2-}, etc., e.g. titanium, zirconium, tin, platinum and palladium.

(3) Finite Polynuclear Molecules

When a molecule contains more than one atom which is poly-covalent, the stereochemistry of each atom can be determined in the normal manner, and then the ways in which these resultant geometrical arrangements can be combined must be considered. A few examples, chosen at random, will serve to illustrate this.

(i) Aluminium chloride

Aluminium chloride in the vapour phase and in solution in such solvents as benzene exists as dimeric molecules, Al_2Cl_6. The dimer is formulated as shown in Fig. 56a, which satisfies normal valency requirements. Each aluminium atom has a valency group of a four-covalent octet and should therefore be surrounded tetrahedrally by chlorine atoms; the two bridging chlorine atoms have a dicovalent octet, so that the bond angle Al—Cl—Al should be somewhat less than 109°, and these conditions are fulfilled in the structure (Fig. 56b) which can be regarded as two tetrahedra sharing an edge.

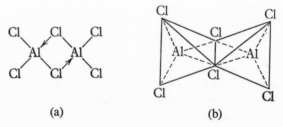

(a)   (b)

FIG. 56 The molecule of aluminium chloride.

(ii) Disulphur decafluoride, S_2F_{10}

The structure of sulphur hexafluoride was seen on p. 99 to consist of an octahedral arrangement of six fluorine atoms around a sulphur atom.

Sulphur also forms a compound disulphur decafluoride, and the structure of this molecule is derived from two SF_6 octahedra as shown in Fig. 57.

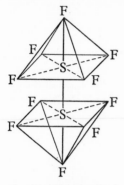

FIG. 57 The molecule of
disulphur decafluoride.

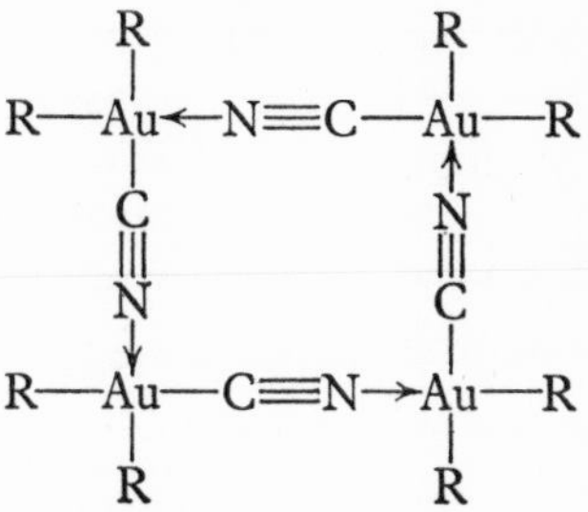

FIG. 58 A tetrameric molecule of a
dialkyl gold(III) cyanide.

(iii) Dialkyl gold(III) cyanides, $R_2Au(CN)$

This series of compounds where R represents different alkyl groups, are known to be tetrameric. Gold(III) has the electronic configuration d^8 (it is isoelectronic with platinum(II)) so that it would be expected to have a square planar coordination. This is not possible if the compounds are monomeric, but does become possible if the compounds form tetrameric molecules as shown in Fig. 58. Each carbon and nitrogen atom forms two σ bonds (and two π bonds) and has a dicovalent quartet as its valency group and hence a linear arrangement of bonds (cf. the ion $[Ag(CN)_2]^-$, p. 120), so that the entire skeleton as represented is planar with bond angles of 90° and 180° as shown.

(iv) The Phosphorus Oxides

The formulae of the phosphorus oxides are often written as P_2O_3 and P_2O_5 and in consequence they are usually called phosphorus tri- and pent-oxide respectively. Their correct molecular formulae are P_4O_6 and P_4O_{10}, however, and their structures can be related simply to that of the phosphorus molecule P_4, see p. 128, from which they can be made by oxidation. In the molecule P_4 each phosphorus atom, being at an apex of a tetrahedron, has a pyramidal distribution of bonds to three other phosphorus atoms (see Fig. 59a), giving a bond angle of 60° which, as was pointed out previously, is a lower value than expected so that there is some strain in the molecule. The molecule P_4O_6 retains the same arrangement of phosphorus atoms and the valency group of a three-covalent octet for each; the oxygen atoms are incorporated in the structure in such a way that there is an oxygen 'bridge' between each pair of phosphorus atoms (a tetrahedron has six edges), as shown in Fig. 59b. Each oxygen atom has a valency group of a di-covalent octet and in accordance with this the P—O—P bond angle should be approximately 109° (actually it is about 125°). This makes it impossible for the oxygen atom to lie on the line joining the nuclei of two phosphorus atoms, i.e. it lies off the edge of the tetrahedron, and as a result there is an increase in the bond angles of the pyramidal structure of bonds from the phosphorus atoms, thereby diminishing the strain.

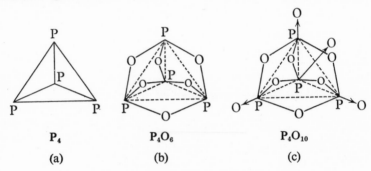

P_4 P_4O_6 P_4O_{10}

(a)   (b)   (c)

Fig. 59 The molecules of phosphorus and its oxides.

The molecule of P_4O_{10} is derived from the molecule of P_4O_6 by adding a further oxygen atom to each phosphorus atom at the apices of the tetrahedron; the bonds used are formally dative covalent bonds, since each electron pair was already pointing in the appropriate direction in space in a convenient orientation to be donated to an oxygen atom. Each phosphorus atom now has a four- instead of a three-covalent octet, and is surrounded by four oxygen atoms arranged tetrahedrally, Fig. 59c. It was seen that the PO_4^{3-} ion has a tetrahedral structure (p. 96), and the molecule of P_4O_{10} can be regarded as being built of four PO_4 tetrahedra, each of which shares three corners with adjacent tetrahedra. (In the same way the structure of the P_4O_6 molecule is built from pyramidal PO_3 units such as are found in the PO_3^{3-} ion.) Such a molecule as that of P_4O_{10} well illustrates the necessity of thinking in three dimensions about the structures of compounds. The structures of other oxides and sulphides of group V elements have features in common with the structures of the phosphorus oxides.

(v) Silicon disulphide, SiS₂, and copper(II) chloride, CuCl₂

The compounds silicon sulphide and anhydrous copper(II) chloride both form chain-like structures, as shown in Figs. 60a and 61a. Silicon is a *p* block element, and its stereochemistry is predicted (Chapter 5) on the grounds that its atom has a four-covalent octet and hence it is tetrahedrally coordinated as shown in Fig. 60b. Copper, on the other hand, is a *d* block

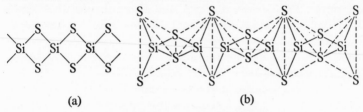

(a)   (b)

FIG. 60 The structure of silicon sulphide.

element, and as has been seen previously (Chapter 6), a distorted octahedra coordination is to be expected from the electronic configuration d^9 of copper(II). This arrangement is achieved by forming planar chains in which each copper atom is surrounded by a square arrangement of chlorine atoms, and the neighbouring chains are so arranged that their chlorine atoms complete the octahedral coordination of the copper atoms in other chains, Fig. 61b.

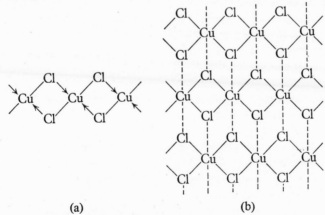

(a)   (b)

FIG. 61 The structure of copper(II) chloride.

(4) Polyanions

The structures of many simple mono-nuclear ions have been described in the two preceding chapters. There are many compounds whose

K

structures can be regarded as built by the condensation of simple ions, e.g. borate, sulphate, vanadate, phosphate, silicate, etc., to form 'polymerised' or polynuclear anions. Of these simple ions, the borate ion alone is planar, whereas the remainder are tetrahedral. Other examples of polynuclear anions are known which are built of octahedral units such as MoO_6^{6-} and WO_6^{6-} although in these cases the simple mononuclear ion itself is not known. These are called iso-poly acid anions, the prefix *iso-* denoting that except for oxygen all the atoms of the anion are of the *same* element. There are also hetero-poly acid anions, the prefix *hetero-* denoting that there is *more than one* element other than oxygen; an example of the anion of a heteropoly acid is the familiar phosphomolybdate ion, $[PMo_{12}O_{40}]^{3-}$, formed by the interaction of phosphate and molybdate ions in solution, which is built of a PO_4 unit surrounded by MoO_6 units which share corners with each other.

Since it is not the purpose of this book to be exhaustive, only the poly-silicates of these various polynuclear ions will be considered in detail, since they are perhaps the most diverse in character and best understood of the various compounds which contain polynuclear anions in their structures, and their structures illustrate many important principles.

A vast number of mineral silicates occur in Nature and the structure of each comprises an anionic framework built of silicon and oxygen atoms, and frequently also aluminium atoms and hydroxyl ions; the negative charge on this framework is balanced by various cations situated throughout the lattice in sites of appropriate coordination. The various anionic frameworks are built up from SiO_4 tetrahedral units (sometimes AlO_4 units also, see later) condensing together in different ways, and it is convenient to classify these before considering individual structures and the arrangement of the cations. This classification considers the ways in which the condensation of the tetrahedra takes place, see Fig. 63.

(A) SiO_4 units are discrete, no corners being shared with adjacent tetrahedra.

(B) Two SiO_4 units share one corner between them.

(C) Each SiO_4 unit shares two corners with adjacent tetrahedra. This may lead to (i) ring formation or (ii) chain formation (cf. the structures of the different forms of sulphur).

(D) Alternate SiO_4 units share two and three corners with adjacent tetrahedra.

(E) Each SiO_4 unit shares three corners with adjacent tetrahedra.

(F) Each SiO_4 unit shares four corners with adjacent tetrahedra.

These six classes will now be considered in turn, with reference to individual structures within the various classes.

Class A is represented by the mineral* olivine, $(Mg, Fe)_2SiO_4$, whose structure was described in Chapter 3, p. 72. It should be noted that the SiO_4 tetrahedra are discrete in that they do not share corners, i.e. oxygen atoms, with adjacent tetrahedra, but they are not widely separated from one another, as are, for example, the sulphate ions in the lattice of sodium sulphate. The metal ions in olivine, i.e. Fe^{2+} and Mg^{2+}, occupy sites of octahedral coordination. This would be predicted from calculations using radius ratio, and such calculations are probably the best approach for predicting the coordination of a metal ion in a silicate lattice; they must be somewhat approximate, however, since the oxygen atoms are bonded to the silicon atoms by bonds of largely covalent character, and to assume an ionic radius for O^{2-} in calculations is not therefore very accurate. In general, the coordination of a metal ion increases with its ionic radius.

The variable composition of olivine which can be between $Mg_0Fe_2SiO_4$ and $Mg_2Fe_0SiO_4$ is understandable when it is realised that these minerals crystallised from a magma containing many elements, and that the main consideration was probably that the charge on the ion was sufficient to balance the negative charge on the silicate lattice, and also that the size of the ion was such that it could fit into the available site. Isomorphous replacement of one ion by another does not take place unless the two ions are of comparable size.

Olivine, on account of its close-packed structure, is a dense mineral (compared with other silicate minerals) and is difficult to fracture. Other minerals of this class include phenacite, Be_2SiO_4, and zircon, $ZrSiO_4$, in which the smaller beryllium and the larger zirconium ions occupy sites of four-fold and eight-fold coordination respectively in lattices which are not related to close-packing.

Class B has features in common with class A in that the ions $Si_2O_7^{6-}$ are discrete; few examples are known, however, so that this class will not be considered further.

The best known example of *class C* (i) is the mineral beryl, $Be_3Al_2Si_6O_{18}$; its structure is built of Si_6O_{18} rings which comprise six SiO_4 tetrahedra, each of which shares two corners with neighbouring tetrahedra, and these are stacked one above the other, with the stacks 'cemented' together by beryllium ions in four-fold and aluminium ions in six-fold coordination (Fig. 62). Minerals are also known in which the silicate lattice comprises

* The term mineral is used in preference to the term compound, since the latter mplies a constancy of composition which is not found in silicate materials.

rings of three SiO_4 tetrahedra linked together as shown in Fig. 63, the anion being $Si_3O_9{}^{6-}$.

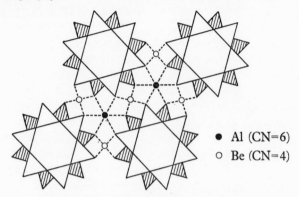

Al (CN=6)

Be (CN=4)

FIG. 62 The Structure of beryl (diagrammatic).

Many minerals are known which have the chain-like silicate structure of *class C* (ii) and these are known collectively as the pyroxene minerals; perhaps the best known examples are enstatite, $MgSiO_3$, and diopside, $CaMg(SiO_3)_2$. In order to visualise the essential features of a pyroxene structure it is necessary to represent the cross-section of a silicate chain by a trapezoid shape which is derived by looking along a chain in the direction shown by the arrow in Fig. 63, see Fig. 64a. The silicate chains pack together as shown in Fig. 64b, which is viewed down the axis of the chains. The cations occupy sites between the chains holding them together; in the case of diopside, the magnesium ions are six-coordinate whereas the larger calcium ions are eight-coordinate.

The anionic frameworks of the *class D* silicates are very similar to those of class C (ii), but are built of double instead of single chains; the minerals of this class are known collectively as the amphibole minerals and a further difference from the pyroxenes is that these always have OH groups incorporated in their structures in addition to the silicon-oxygen chains and the cations. Examples of amphiboles are tremolite, $Ca_2Mg_5(Si_4O_{11})_2(OH)_2$, and crocidolite, $Na_2(Fe^{II},Mg)_3Fe_2{}^{III}(Si_4O_{11})_2(OH)_2$. The cross-section of an amphibole chain, like that of a pyroxene chain, is trapezoid in shape, Fig. 65a, and the chains are held together in a similar manner. Most asbestos minerals are amphiboles, so that the chain-like nature of their structure is reflected in the bulk properties of the minerals.

An elegant correlation between the physical properties of a material and its molecular constitution is afforded by the characteristic cleavage

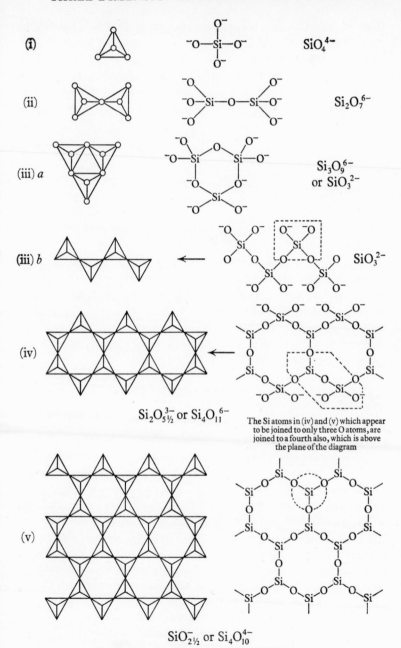

FIG. 63 A structural classification of mineral silicates.

angles shown by amphiboles and pyroxenes. A crystal of an amphibole or a pyroxene comprises a large number of chains orientated parallel to each other, as in Figs. 64*b* and 65*b*. When a crystal is split parallel to the chain axes the fragments cleave apart. When these fragments are viewed down the chain axes by means of a microscope the angle of cleavage can be measured and it is found that all amphiboles have the same angle of

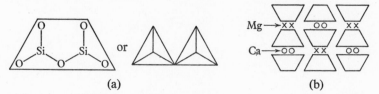

(a)   (b)

Fig. 64 (*a*) a cross-section through a pyroxene chain, and (*b*) the structure of diopside (diagrammatic).

cleavage, i.e. 57°, and that all pyroxenes have the same angle of cleavage, i.e. 89°; the two classes of mineral can be differentiated by their characteristic cleavage angle. The line of cleavage of the minerals follows those directions in which the smallest numbers of ions are situated, i.e. the directions in which the bonding is weakest. The explanation of how this difference in cleavage angle can arise can be seen by reference to Fig. 66.

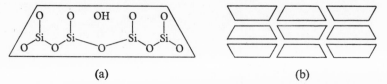

(a)   (b)

Fig. 65 A cross-section through an amphibole chain, and (*b*) the stacking of these chains.

The silicate framework illustrated in Fig. 63 for *class E* minerals is seen to comprise tetrahedra all of which have their apices pointing up out of the plane of the paper. Hence in this sheet structure there are two layers of oxygen atoms; the lower layer comprises the bases of all the tetrahedra and contains a greater number of oxygen atoms than the upper layer; the silicon atoms are situated in tetrahedral coordination between the two layers. The minerals which have this type of silicate framework all contain OH groups also. In the simplest of these structures, typified by kaolinite, $Al_4(OH)_8Si_4O_{10}$, the second layer of oxygen atoms is augmented by some OH groups and a third layer is added which comprises OH groups only. The composite structure is thus of three layers of oxygen

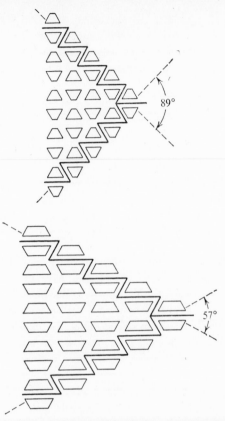

FIG. 66 Cleavage of amphiboles and pyroxenes. The eight apices lie
at the corners of two mutually perpendicular squares, which have
a common centre.

atoms and hydroxyl groups in an arrangement which is not very different
from close-packing with silicon atoms situated in tetrahedral sites between
two of the layers, and the aluminium atoms are in octahedral sites between
the other two layers, as is shown diagrammatically in Fig. 67a.

In the mineral pyrophillite, $Al_2(OH)_2Si_4O_{10}$, this type of packing of
layers is extended so that there is a silicate sheet on both sides of the
hydroxyl layer, as shown in Fig. 67b. In these structures the aluminium
atoms occupy only two of every three available octahedral sites (cf. the
structure of corundum), and corresponding minerals are known in which
all three sites are occupied by magnesium atoms, which are similar in
size, but three atoms of the dipositive magnesium are required to balance
the same charge on the silicate framework as two atoms of the tripositive

aluminium. These minerals are chrysotile, $Mg_6(OH)_8Si_4O_{10}$, and talc, $Mg_3(OH)_2Si_4O_{10}$. It is clear from the diagrams that there are no strong forces available to hold the composite layers together, and in consequence minerals of this class are soft and cleave easily into sheets.

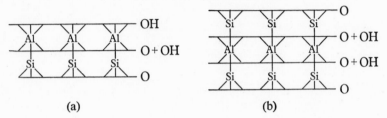

(a)   (b)

FIG. 67 The structures of (a) kaolinite and (b) pyrophillite (diagrammatic).

There are many other mineral silicates which have a layer structure and belong to this class, and many of these have an additional feature which has not been referred to previously, in that some aluminium atoms occupy tetrahedral sites. This is possible for aluminium atoms because they are very similar in size to silicon atoms, and the radius ratio value of r_{Al}/r_O is close to the limiting value observed for a change from tetrahedral to octahedral coordination. (Aluminium in octahedral coordination has been referred to above.) However, the AlO_4 tetrahedron bears a charge of -5 compared with the charge of -4 on an SiO_4 tetrahedron, and this additional negative charge must be balanced by the simultaneous incorporation of a cation into the lattice.

The formulae of these silicates, examples of which are muscovite and margarite, can be derived from the formula of pyrophillite (above) by replacing one-quarter or one-half of the silicon atoms (and hence a like proportion of the SiO_4 tetrahedra) by aluminium atoms and introducing a monovalent or divalent cation respectively to balance the added charge; thus, $Si_4O_{10}{}^{4-}$ becomes successively $K^+[AlSi_3O_{10}]^{5-}$ and $Ca^{2+}[Al_2Si_2O_{10}]^{6-}$. The complete formulae then become:

$$Al_2(OH)_2(Si_4O_{10}) \qquad \text{pyrophillite}$$
$$KAl_2(OH)_2(AlSi_3O_{10}) \qquad \text{muscovite}$$
$$CaAl_2(OH)_2(Al_2Si_2O_{10}) \qquad \text{margarite.}$$

These formulae are written in this way, with the aluminium in two places to denote the dual role of that element in occupying sites of both four- and six-fold coordination, and also so that it is possible to determine the class of the mineral, since the relation to $Si_4O_{10}^{4-}$ is preserved in the aluminosilicates. The additional cations, i.e. potassium and calcium respectively, are accommodated between the composite layers as shown in Fig. 68, and as they are relatively large cations they occupy sites of eight- and twelve-fold coordination. On account of these electrostatic bonds, the sheets are held together more strongly than in pyrophillite, etc.

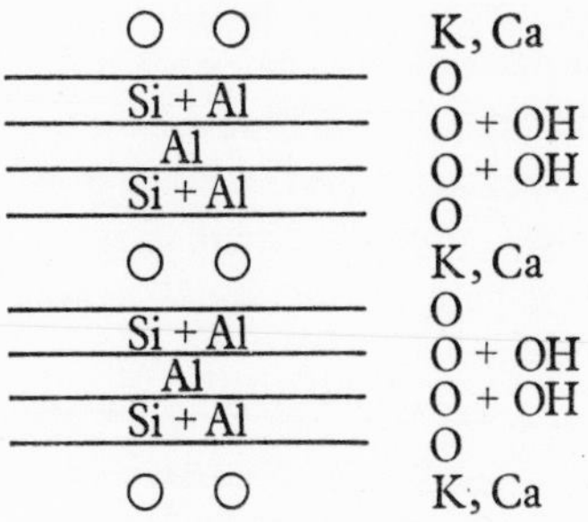

The minerals muscovite and margarite, etc., belong to the group known as the micas and their layer type of structure is reflected in their characteristic property of being easily split into sheets, margarite with more difficulty than muscovite because of the greater forces of attraction associated with a divalent cation (cf. CaO harder than NaCl, although both have the same structural arrangement). On account of this, margarite is known as a brittle mica.

O O	K, Ca
	O
Si + Al	O + OH
Al	O + OH
Si + Al	O
O O	K, Ca
	O
Si + Al	O + OH
Al	O + OH
Si + Al	O
O O	K, Ca

FIG. 68 The structure of micas (diagrammatic).

If each SiO_4 tetrahedron shares each oxygen atom, i.e. corner, with adjacent tetrahedra the compound silicon dioxide results and the structure of one form of this has already been described (see β-cristobalite, Chapter 3, p. 62). If, however, a proportion of the SiO_4 tetrahedra is replaced by AlO_4 tetrahedra, then some cations must be introduced to balance the additional negative charge and then a material results which can be described as an aluminosilicate. Minerals with structures of *class F* must be aluminosilicates, and since every oxygen atom of every tetrahedron is shared, compact three-dimensional lattices are formed. The best known examples of this class are the felspars, e.g. orthoclase $KAlSi_3O_8$. The structures will not be described in detail. Since there is Si—O bonding in all directions these minerals are harder than the micas, etc., but are not as hard as quartz, which has no electrostatic bonds in its structure.

A sequence of certain minerals in order of increasing hardness is:

talc $<$ muscovite $<$ margarite $<$ orthoclase $<$ quartz,

and this order can be understood by a consideration of the molecular structures of the various minerals as described above.

Further examples of class F silicates are ultramarine and the zeolites. These latter, unlike other silicate minerals considered previously, contain many water molecules in the crystal lattice, e.g. chabazite, $(Na_2,Ca)(Al_2Si_4O_{12})6H_2O$. These water molecules can be removed from many of the zeolites by the action of heat *in vacuo*, when there remains an open-work aluminosilicate lattice traversed by channels in which the water molecules had previously been situated. The dehydrated zeolites can adsorb small molecules, but not large ones, in these channels, and they have been termed 'Molecular Sieves' on account of their ability to separate small molecules from large ones. They have also a strong affinity for regaining the lost water molecules and hence can act as very powerful desiccants.

In this brief survey of the structures of some mineral silicates the more important principles have been outlined, i.e. the condensation of SiO_4 and AlO_4 tetrahedra in different ways to form anionic frameworks whose charges are balanced by cations which occupy sites of appropriate co-ordination and size, and some correlations between physical properties and molecular structure have been pointed out.

DEFECTS IN THE SOLID STATE

Introduction

Descriptions of the crystal structures of many compounds which have three-dimensional lattices in which no discrete molecules can be detected were given in Chapters 3 and 4; in describing these, emphasis was placed on the regularity of the atomic arrangements in the solid state. No crystal structure is perfect, however, and in this chapter consideration will be given to some kinds of known imperfections and their consequences. For the sake of simplicity, the discussion will be restricted to compounds of type AB, although similar arguments apply to other compounds also, and it will be more convenient in discussing defects to regard these compounds as being mainly ionic, even although, as was pointed out in previous chapters, some of them have appreciable covalent character.

In an ideal crystal of type AB the number of atoms of A is exactly equal to the number of atoms of B (i.e. the compound is stoichiometric), each atom is surrounded regularly by the appropriate arrangement of atoms of the other kind, and no site which should be occupied is vacant, i.e. both the cation lattice and the anion lattice are complete. In real crystals, however, some sites can be unoccupied so that either the cation lattice or the anion lattice or both are incomplete, some atoms can occupy sites of a different coordination from that expected, and in some compounds the number of atoms of A is not exactly equal to the number of atoms of B; when this last is the case the compound is said to be non-stoichiometric. In the following discussion stoichiometric and non-stoichiometric compounds will be considered in turn.

Defects in Stoichiometric Crystals

Any compound in which the arrangement of the constituent atoms in the crystal lattice is not completely regular is non-ideal or defective. Thus, in mineral silicates, spinels, ilmenite, etc., where atoms of more than one element are distributed in a random way on sites of a particular kind, the lattice is not completely regular so that these structures are defective; these defects are specific to each individual compound. It can be shown that, at temperatures above the absolute zero, it is thermodynamically necessary for crystal lattices to contain defects. There are two kinds of thermodynamic defect: (i) Schottky defects and (ii) Frenkel defects.

A Schottky defect consists of a vacant cation site *and* a vacant anion site; the two missing atoms are considered to have migrated to the surface of the crystal. In a crystal which contains Schottky defects both the cation and the anion lattices are incomplete.

A Frenkel defect consists of a vacant lattice site, with the atom which ideally should have occupied that site occupying a different type of position in the lattice such as is vacant in the perfect crystal. In some crystals Frenkel defects produce an incomplete cation lattice whereas other crystals have an incomplete anion lattice; an incomplete cation lattice is more common since cations are in general smaller than anions and hence can be more easily squeezed into the alternative interstitial positions. These alternative positions can have a different coordination, so that, for example, a Frenkel defect in a zinc blende crystal might result in a zinc atom occupying an octahedral site (and these are normally unoccupied, see p. 55) while the tetrahedral site which it normally occupies is left vacant.

The term 'interstitial' as it is applied to atoms in defect structures implies that the site so occupied is interstitial with respect to both the cation and the anion lattices, whereas when the term was used in earlier chapters it implied that the sites which were interstitial in one lattice were occupied by the atoms of the other lattice.

Schottky and Frenkel defects are illustrated diagramatically in Fig. 69. for a hypothetical two-dimensional network of a crystal of type AB.

A^+	B^-	A^+	B^-	A^+	B^-		A^+	B^-	A^+	B^-	A^+	B^-

$$A^+ \ B^- \ A^+ \ B^- \ A^+ \ B^- \qquad A^+ \ B^- \ A^+ \ B^- \ A^+ \ B^-$$
$$\qquad\qquad\qquad\qquad\qquad\qquad\qquad A^+$$
$$B^- \qquad\quad B^- \qquad\quad B^- \ A^+ \ B^- \qquad B^- \qquad\quad B^- \ A^+ \ B^- \ A^+$$

$$A^+ \ B^- \ A^+ \ B^- \ A^+ \ B^- \ A^+ \qquad A^+ \ B^- \ A^+ \ B^- \ A^+ \ B^-$$

$$B^- \ A^+ \qquad\quad A^+ \qquad\quad A^+ \ B^- \qquad B^- \ A^+ \ B^- \ A^+ \ B^- \ A^+$$
$$\qquad\qquad\qquad\qquad\qquad\qquad\qquad A^+$$
$$A^+ \ B^- \ A^+ \ B^- \ A^+ \ B^- \ A^+ \qquad A^+ \ B^- \ A^+ \ B^- \qquad\quad B^-$$

$$B^- \ A^+ \ B^- \ A^+ \ B^- \ A^+ \qquad B^- \ A^+ \ B^- \ A^+ \ B^- \ A^+$$

Schottky defects   Frenkel defects

FIG. 69 Schottky and Frenkel defects.

It can be shown that, for a crystal AB, the number of Schottky defects is given by the expression:

$$n_s = Ne^{-\frac{W_s}{2kT}},$$

where n_s is the number of Schottky defects per c.c. of the crystal at $T°$ K; i.e. there are n_s vacant cation sites and n_s vacant anion sites.

N is the number of ion pairs per c.c. of an ideal crystal, i.e. assuming it to contain no defects; there are therefore N possible cation sites and N possible anion sites.

W_s is the work required to form a Schottky defect, i.e. to transport an ion pair to the surface of a crystal.

The above expression for n_s assumes that $N \gg n_s$, i.e. that the crystal, is not grossly defective.

Similarly, the number of Frenkel defects is given by:

$$n_f = \sqrt{NN'}e^{-\frac{W_f}{2kT}},$$

where n_f is the number of Frenkel defects per c.c. of the crystal at $T°$ K.

N is the number of sites per c.c. of the ideal crystal of the type which are left vacant on formation of Frenkel defects.

N' is the number of alternative interstitial positions per c.c. of the crystal which are available.

W_f is the work required to form a Frenkel defect.

Thus it can be seen that the concentration of defects of either type in a given crystal is dependent upon the energy required to produce them and upon the absolute temperature; the number of defects increases with an increase of temperature.

Although any crystal contains both types of defect, one type or the other normally predominates. The concentrations of the two types of defect would be the same only if the energies required to form each were identical, and this is not usually so. In most crystals the energy required to form a Schottky defect is less than that required to form a Frenkel defect. Frenkel defects are more easily formed in those compounds in which the constituent ions are easily distorted; such compounds are formed by strongly polarising cations and easily polarisable anions, and are thus compounds of appreciably covalent character. The distortion allows the more easy accommodation of an ion, more particularly a cation, in an interstitial site, and also allows a closer approach of oppositely charged ions with a consequent gain in energy; this gain helps to balance the amount of energy which has to be expended in creating the defect. Such distortion leads to a high dielectric constant, (see p. 41), so that Frenkel defects are likely to be favoured by those compounds which have a high dielectric constant.

Frenkel defects are more easily formed in crystals where the ions have a low coordination number since there are fewer attractive interionic forces to resist the migration of an ion to an alternative position; they are also more likely where there is an appreciable difference in size between the cation and the anion, since this makes the interstitial position more appropriate in size to contain the interstitial ion (cf. the section on radius ratio, p. 80).

In most of the alkali halides there is not a great disparity in size between cation and anion, and polarisation is not appreciable since the cations have inert gas type of electronic configurations, so that these crystals contain Schottky defects almost exclusively. Such compounds as adopt the zinc blende and wurtzite structures, which have a lower coordination number than the sodium chloride and caesium chloride structures, more often show a disparity in ionic size and the extent of polarisation is more marked—the cations are frequently those which do not have inert gas type of configuration—so that these crystals contain mainly Frenkel defects.

The implications of the existence of defects can be more easily appreciated when an example is considered in some detail. Consider sodium chloride. As would be expected in this crystal, Schottky defects are much more numerous than Frenkel defects and the latter can therefore be neglected. Conductivity measurements (see below) give a value for W_s, the energy required to form a Schottky defect, of 40 K.cals./g.mol. (It is interesting to compare this energy with the lattice energy of sodium chloride which is 180·4 K.cals./g.mol. (see p. 17); the lattice energy is the energy given out when the ions are brought together from infinity to form a crystal lattice, so that this same amount of energy has to be supplied to break down the lattice and move the ions to infinity; in contrast, the energy of defect formation is that required to move the ions only to the surface of the crystal.)

The density of sodium chloride is 2·17 g./c.c. and hence the molecular volume, i.e. molecular weight ÷ density, is $58·46 \div 2·17 = 26·93$ c.c.; thus 26·93 c.c. of a sodium chloride crystal contain $6·06 \times 10^{23}$ (the Avogadro number) ions of each kind, assuming the crystal to be perfect. Hence N, the number of ion pairs per c.c. of an ideal crystal, is given by

$$N = 6 \cdot 06 \times 10^{23}/26 \cdot 93 = 2 \cdot 25 \times 10^{22}.$$

Now, $$n_s = N e^{-\frac{W_s}{2kT}}.$$

Suppose that $$T = 500° \text{ C.} = 773° \text{ K.},$$

then $$n_s = (2 \cdot 25 \times 10^{22}) \times 2 \cdot 718^{-\frac{40000}{2 \times 1 \cdot 98 \times 773}}$$
$$= 4 \cdot 7 \times 10^{16}.$$

Thus, since the crystal contains $2 \cdot 25 \times 10^{22}$ sites of each kind per c.c., and at 500° C. the number of these vacant is $4 \cdot 7 \times 10^{16}$ (i.e. the number of Schottky defects), it follows that one cation site in 10^6 (one million) and one anion site in 10^6 are vacant, the appropriate ions having migrated to the surface. A similar calculation shows that at room temperature the proportion of sites vacant is one in 10^{15} whereas at 800° C., i.e. just below the melting point of sodium chloride, the figure is one in 10^4.

The presence of defects in a crystal causes some changes in physical properties. When the density of a crystal which contains Schottky defects is measured by a displacement method it should be lower than when it is calculated from X-ray crystallographic data, since in this latter calculation the assumption is made that every lattice point is occupied whereas in reality there are vacant sites. It is possible, however, that the presence of vacant sites will cause a contraction of the lattice, leading to a decrease in unit cell dimensions and the total volume of the crystal, and this will offset the expected decrease in density to some extent. In most cases the difference between the observed and calculated densities is of the same order of magnitude as the experimental error; significant differences have been found in certain crystals, particularly those which are grossly defective. The presence of Frenkel defects in a crystal should not alter its volume, and hence its density also should be unchanged.

Specific heat measurements made on certain selected compounds at high temperatures yielded values which showed deviations from those expected for perfect crystals. To explain these deviations, it was assumed that some of the heat energy being supplied to the crystals was used in forming thermodynamic defects. When calculations based on this assumption were made, values for the energy of defect formation were obtained which agreed well with values obtained by other experimental methods.

It is possible to visualise a mechanism by which ionic solids can carry an electric current only when the existence of defects is taken into account. Perhaps the most valuable method for the determination of energies of defect formation depends upon the measurement of electrical conductivity.

When the conductivity of an ionic compound is measured, it is found to increase with an increase in temperature. This is partially because the ions which carry the current by their movement are more mobile, but also because there is a higher concentration of defects as the temperature is raised. It can be shown that

$$\kappa \propto e^{-\frac{(U + W/2)}{kT}},$$

where κ is the conductivity of an ionic crystal,

U is the activation energy for the migration of an ion,

W is the energy required to form a defect.

Hence a plot of $\ln\kappa$ against $1/T$ gives a straight line, the gradient of which is $-1/k \cdot (U + W/2)$.

Since the value of W is required, that of U must be evaluated by another experiment. A controlled concentration of cations of higher charge is introduced into the compound being studied and the variation of conductivity with temperature is again measured. Since the foreign ions introduced into the lattice have a higher charge than the host cations, some cation vacancies must also result to allow a maintenance of electrical neutrality. The concentration of these artificially produced vacancies is adjusted so that it greatly exceeds the concentration of thermodynamic defects (which latter can then be ignored) and it does not vary with temperature since the composition remains constant. Hence the variation in the conductivity of the 'doped' crystals with temperature is not due to a variation in the concentration of defects but only to the increased mobility of the ions which are carrying the current. These measurements allow the evaluation of U, so that a value for W, the energy of defect formation, is obtained by combining the results of the two experiments.

The mechanism by which an ionic crystal carries an electric current is such that as one ion moves into a neighbouring vacancy thereby leaving its own site vacant, a second ion in its turn moves into this vacant site, and further ions continue this process so that the nett result is transport throughout the entire crystal.

Conduction can involve the movement of cations or anions or both. (In non-stoichiometric crystals, described below, electronic conduction is a further possibility.) Various methods have been employed to determine which species are mobile in particular crystals. Perhaps the best of these is that which utilises radioactive isotopes. A sample of the material is used in which one of the elements is labelled with respect to a radioactive isotope. Initially the distribution of the radioactive isotope is homogeneous throughout the entire crystal, but, if that particular ion is mobile, the radioactivity will become more intense at the side of the crystal nearer the electrode towards which it is moving under the influence of the applied voltage. (The radioactivity can be determined by counting techniques or by the effect of radiation on photographic paper—autoradiography.)

In a crystal which contains predominantly Frenkel defects there are vacancies in only one lattice (usually the cation lattice), so that only one type of ion can be mobile. In a crystal which contains predominantly Schottky defects there are vacancies in both lattices, so that both types of ion can migrate, although it is not a necessary condition that both should do so; which ion or ions do migrate is dependent upon the values of U for the two different types of ion in the particular crystal.

A comparison of potassium chloride with silver bromide shows the essential differences between crystals containing the two types of defect. Potassium chloride contains Schottky defects so that there are both cation and anion vacancies in the crystal; the observed density at high temperatures (at which the concentration of defects becomes large) is less than expected, and the compound conducts by an ionic mechanism, the current being carried by cations only at low temperatures but by anions also at higher temperatures.

Silver bromide on the other hand contains Frenkel defects, so that the crystal contains cation vacancies and hence has cations in interstitial positions in the lattice—the anion lattice is complete; the density of the compound is normal; it conducts by an ionic mechanism and this of necessity involves cations only, since there are no vacancies in the anionic lattice.

Measurements of transport numbers must be made on very pure materials. Thus, for pure potassium chloride at 600° C., Kerkhoff found that the cations carried 71 per cent. of the current, whereas the introduction of as little as 0·02 per cent. of calcium chloride increased that figure to 99 per cent. The introduction of each calcium ion causes an additional vacancy in the cation lattice.

Defects in Non-stoichiometric Crystals

Many apparently simple inorganic compounds are non-stoichiometric, that is the ratio of the number of atoms of one kind to the number of atoms of the other kind does not correspond exactly to the ideal whole number ratio as expressed by the formula. As an example, iron sulphide which is usually written as FeS corresponds much more closely to $Fe_{0.9}S$

L

or to Fe_8S_9 than to the ideal 1:1 composition, and the composition can vary significantly from one sample of the compound to another.

It is clear that such an unbalance of composition is only possible if the structure is in some way irregular, i.e. possesses defects. Such defects are additional to the normal thermodynamic defects; they are similar, however, in that they also involve vacant sites and ions in interstitial positions. Non-stoichiometry means that there is an excess either of metal or of non-metal atoms and there are two ways in which each kind of excess can arise in a crystal lattice. These four possibilities will now be considered in turn, and they are illustrated in Fig. 70.

A^+ B^- A^+ B^- A^+ B^- A^+ B^- A^+ B^- A^+ B^-

                                          e^- A^+

B^- A^+ $\boxed{e^-}$ A^+ B^- A^+ B^- A^+ B^- A^+ B^- A^+

A^+ B^- A^+ B^- A^+ B^- A^+ B^- A^+ B^- A^+ B^-

                                          e^- A^+

B^- A^+ B^- A^+ $\boxed{e^-}$ A^+ B^- A^+ B^- A^+ B^- A^+

A^+ B^- A^+ B^- A^+ B^- A^+ B^- A^+ B^- A^+ B^-

Type I   *Type II*

A^+ B^- A^+ B^- A^+ B^- A^+ B^- A^+ B^- A^{2+} B^-

                                           B^-

B^- $\boxed{}$ B^- A^+ B^- A^+ B^- A^+ B^- A^+ B^- A^+

A^{2+} B^- A^+ B^- A^{2+} B^- A^+ B^- A^+ B^- A^+ B^-

                                           B^-

B^- A^+ B^- $\boxed{}$ B^- A^+ B^- A^{2+} B^- A^+ B^- A^+

A^+ B^- A^+ B^- A^+ B^- A^+ B^- A^+ B^- A^+ B^-

Type III   *Type IV*

FIG. 70 Defects in non-stoichiometric lattices.

Type I—Metal excess due to anion vacancies

This can be regarded as the removal of atoms of the non-metal from the crystal lattice leaving vacancies; to maintain an electrical balance, the electrons which were associated with the anions remain trapped in the vacancies. This can be represented schematically as follows:

B^-(on lattice site)$\rightarrow \frac{1}{2}B_2$(gaseous)+anion vacancy+$e^-$(trapped).

This type of defect is reminiscent of a Schottky defect, but involves vacancies in the anion lattice only. Non-stoichiometry of this type is found in crystals which would be expected to have Schottky rather than Frenkel defects and examples are uncommon.

Type II—Metal excess due to interstitial cations

In this case atoms of the non-metal are lost from the crystal lattice while the electrons previously associated with them remain behind; the excess metal ions are then forced to occupy interstitial sites and the free electrons are trapped in the vicinity of these interstitial cations:

$A^+ + B^-$(on lattice site)$\rightarrow \frac{1}{2}B_2$(gaseous)+$A^+$(interstitial)+$e^-$(trapped near ion).

This type of defect is reminiscent of a Frenkel defect, but there are no cation vacancies to compensate for the interstitial cations. Non-stoichiometry of this type is found in crystals which would be expected to have Frenkel rather than Schottky defects, and it is more common than the previous type.

Type III—Metal deficiency due to cation vacancies

In this case it is considered that the lattice acquires additional atoms of the non-metal which gain electrons to become anions. These electrons are obtained from the crystal as some of the metal ions are oxidised to a higher oxidation state:

$A^+ \rightarrow A^{2+}$(on the same lattice site)+e^-(which diffuses to the surface of the crystal)

$\frac{1}{2}B_2$(gaseous)+e^-(on the surface)$\rightarrow B^-$(on a lattice site)+cation vacancy.

Thus the number of anions in the crystal is increased without any compensating increase in the number of cations, so that the crystal has a complete anion lattice but an incomplete cation lattice. The existing cations migrate and distribute themselves over the enlarged anion lattice so that the resulting cation vacancies are also uniformly distributed.

Type IV—Metal deficiency due to interstitial anions

In this case, as in the previous one, the lattice acquires additional atoms of the non-metal which become anions by gaining electrons as a result of the oxidation of some of the metal ions. The added anions, however, occupy interstitial positions:

$A^+ \rightarrow A^{2+}$(on the same lattice site)$+e^-$(which diffuses to the surface of the crystal)

$\frac{1}{2}B_2$(gaseous)$+e^-$(on the surface)$\rightarrow B^-$(penetrates the lattice to an interstitial position).

The crystal thus has complete cation and anion lattices with no vacancies to compensate for the interstitial anions. Since anions are larger than cations this would seem an unlikely way of achieving non-stoichiometry and indeed no examples of it seem to have been found.

In Types III and IV which are metal deficient, there are no free electrons in the crystal as there are in Types I and II which have excess metal; there are, however, cations of the same metal in different oxidation states. It follows that metal deficiency is only likely to be found in compounds of those metals which can display different oxidation states in their compounds; this is a general characteristic of the transition metals.

The existence of electrons trapped in the crystal lattice which was seen to be a feature of Types I and II results in a compound having such properties as might be expected by analogy with a hydrogen or an alkali metal atom. Thus, the electrons can be excited to a higher energy level and hence absorption spectra can be measured. Many such compounds are coloured. When a crystal of an alkali halide is heated in the vapour of its constituent metal it becomes non-stoichiometric with a metal excess. There is little or no polarisation in these crystals so that Schottky-type defects are to be expected; accordingly, the non-stoichiometry is of type I. The non-stoichiometric crystals are coloured—the sodium halides yellow, and the potassium halides lilac—colours which recall the flame colourations due to these metals.

The trapped electrons of Type I and II non-stoichiometric compounds are not localised but can be ionised and can move throughout the entire lattice. In consequence such compounds are good electrical conductors, the current being carried not by ions but by the free electrons. The conductivity of these compounds is intermediate between that of the metals, which have many more electrons available for conduction, and the so-called insulators, which conduct, if at all, by ionic mechanisms. Accordingly the compounds belong to the class of materials known as semi-conductors.

Those non-stoichiometric compounds which are metal-deficient are also semi-conductors, i.e. their conductivity is comparable with that of the metal-excess compounds, but the mechanism of conduction is different since they have no free electrons. The crystal lattices of these compounds contain ions of the same metal in different oxidation states; under a potential difference an electron can switch from one ion in the lower oxidation state to an ion in the higher oxidation state (thereby reversing the charges which these ions carried originally) and the multiplication of this process enables electrons to travel across the crystal and thus to conduct a current. As an electron moves aross the crystal in one direction a metal ion in the higher oxidation state appears to move in the opposite direction, although in reality the cations do not move at all; the 'local excess of positive charge' that such an ion represents is referred to as 'a positive hole'.

Non-stoichiometric compounds can thus be divided into:

(1) metal-excess compounds, which are *n*-type semi-conductors, i.e. *n*ormal electron conduction mechanism.
(2) metal-deficient compounds, which are *p*-type semi-conductors, i.e. *p*ositive hole conduction mechanisms.

The existence of non-stoichiometry is often detectable by chemical analysis, although the unbalance in composition is frequently too small to be detected by this means; analysis does not provide information about the existence of vacant sites or interstitial ions and hence the type of non-stoichiometry. Differences between the observed and calculated densities can be informative, but as was pointed out on p. 151. such information must be considered carefully. The presence of interstitial ions would be expected to lead to an increase in the number of ions within unit volume and therefore to an increase in density, but this would be cancelled out if these interstitial ions caused the crystal to expand. The presence of vacancies would be expected to produce a decrease in the number of atoms per unit volume and therefore to produce a decrease in density, but this would be off-set if the existence of vacancies caused the crystal lattice to contract. A further complication is introduced by the oxidation of a proportion of the metal ions in metal deficient compounds to a higher oxidation state since these ions are smaller (see p. 29) and their presence might be expected to produce some contraction in the lattice and thus an increase in density.

Evidence concerning the non-stoichiometry of a compound can be obtained from conductivity measurements. A comparison of the conductivity of a pure compound with the conductivity of the same compound previously 'doped' by the introduction of some cations of a lower oxidation state is particularly useful. If the non-stoichiometric compound is a p-type semi-conductor, i.e. metal deficient, the addition of each low-valence ion will necessitate the oxidation of one ion of the metal in the compound to its higher oxidation state in order to maintain electrical balance, and this will enhance the conductivity. If, however, the non-stoichiometric compound is an n-type semi-conductor, i.e. metal excessive, each low-valence cation added will capture one of the free electrons and lead to a decrease in the conductivity.

A similar technique is the heating of the non-stoichiometric compound AB to a high temperature in an atmosphere of B_2 at high pressure. Some atoms of B will gain electrons from the crystal and add on to the lattice as B^- ions. If AB is an n-type semi-conductor the loss of electrons will cause its conductivity to decrease, whereas if it is a p-type semi-conductor the loss of electrons will cause further atoms to be oxidised to the higher oxidation state and thus increase the conductivity.

It was seen above that the more likely types of non-stoichiometry are (1) metal excess with interstitial cations and a complete anion lattice, and (2) metal deficiency with cation vacancies and again a complete anion lattice. It can be shown that the number of interstitial ions, n_i, and the number of vacancies, n_v, in these two types are given respectively by the expressions:

$$n_i = N'p^{-\frac{1}{2}}e^{-\frac{W_f + W_B}{kT}}$$

and
$$n_v = Np^{\frac{1}{2}}e^{\frac{W_B}{kT}},$$

where W_B is the energy given out when one B^- ion is added to the crystal,

  W_f is the energy required to form a Frenkel defect, and hence $W_f = W_i + W_v$,

  N is the number of cation sites in 1 c.c. of the crystal,

  N' is the number of possible interstitial sites in 1 c.c. of the crystal,

  p is the pressure of B_2 above the crystal.

The extent of the non-stoichiometry of a compound is seen to be dependent upon the temperature, upon the energy required to form a defect and upon the pressure of B_2. Thus, when any non-stoichiometric crystal is formed it is in equilibrium with a particular pressure of B_2, although, since the crystals are stable at ordinary temperatures in the absence of a pressure of B_2, the equilibrium is presumably frozen due to the lack of mobility of the constituent ions.

It has been shown that the larger the number of Frenkel defects which a stoichiometric crystal of AB contains, the smaller is the difference in the pressure of B_2 which is required to produce non-stoichiometry. That is, compounds which contain the greatest concentration of Frenkel defects under ideal conditions are those which are the most likely to be non-stoichiometric.

Non-stoichiometric compounds can exist over a range of composition and that range is likely to be appreciable if

(i) the energy required to form defects is not large;

(ii) the energies of the different oxidation states of the metal are not very different, i.e. the ionisation potential of the additional electron is not high;

(iii) the sizes of the ions of the two different oxidation states are similar since otherwise lattice collapse is likely.

There are some compounds such as FeO and FeS for which an exactly stoichiometric composition is thermodynamically unstable.

Note that non-stoichiometry is likely in compounds where the metal can form stable ions in more than one oxidation state and when these ions are strongly polarising; also when the non-metal anions are readily polarisable. Non-stoichiometry is thus most often displayed by compounds of the transition metals with anions which are large or have a charge greater than unity.

Some examples of compounds which display non-stoichiometry will now be considered. It has already been pointed out, p. 156, that the alkali metal halides can take up excess metal and thus show non-stoichiometry of Type I; a further example of this type which will be discussed below is titanium(II) oxide. It is a familiar characteristic of zinc oxide that it is white when cold but yellow when hot, and this colour is associated with non-stoichiometry. At high temperatures the compound is non-stoichiometric with a metal excess which is incorporated as interstitial cations, i.e. Type II. It is thus an n-type semi-conductor.

The compounds FeO, FeS and NiO are examples of metal-deficient non-stoichiometry of Type III, i.e. each has a complete anion lattice but with cation vacancies. These compounds are p-type semi-conductors,

Some measurements which were made on FeO serve to illustrate the effect of variation in chemical composition on such physical properties as the density of the solid (cf. p. 151) and the size of the unit cell. FeO adopts the sodium chloride structure and thus has a cubic unit cell. Both the density of the material and the length of the unit cell were observed to decrease as the proportion of iron in the compound decreased (or the proportion of oxygen increased). This evidence requires that the deficit of iron is due to vacancies in the cation lattice, since the alternative of interstitial oxygen ions would necessitate an increase both in density and in unit cell length. Some values are quoted below:

Atomic ratio Fe/O	Density (c.c./g.)	Cell length (Å)
0·944	5·725	4·2997
0·932	5·658	4·2920
0·929	5·643	4·2909
0·918	5·624	4·2847
0·911	5·613	4·2816

Whereas samples of FeO with compositions intermediate between $Fe_{0.95}O$ and $Fe_{0.91}O$ are thermodynamically stable, compositions outside this range including the stoichiometric ratio of 1:1 are unstable, the stoichiometric ratio with respect to metallic iron and the oxide Fe_3O_4 (magnetite). Thus, although FeO and Fe_3O_4 have similar structures (see p. 88), and it is easy to visualise a mechanism for their interconversion, the complete range of composition is not thermodynamically stable.

A compound which can exist over a particularly wide range of composition is titanium(II) oxide, TiO. This compound, which also adopts the sodium chloride structure, is stable for any composition between the limits $TiO_{0.69}$ and $TiO_{1.33}$; (the latter is better written as $Ti_{0.75}O$ since it is the cation lattice which is incomplete). Physical measurements have shown that the stoichiometric compound contains a high concentration of Schottky defects, such that 15 per cent. of both cation and anion sites are vacant. At the metal rich end of the composition range, the metal lattice is 96 per cent. complete and the oxygen lattice only 66 per cent. The non-stoichiometry is therefore of Type I and n-type semi-conductivity would be expected. At the oxygen rich end, 98 per cent. of the oxygen sites are occupied but only 74 per cent. of the metal sites, so that the non-stoichiometry is of Type III and p-type semi-conductivity would be expected.

Composition	Ti sites occupied %	O sites occupied %	Conductivity
$TiO_{1.33}$*	74	98	p-type
TiO	85	85	ionic
$TiO_{0.69}$	96	66	n-type

* See note in preceding paragraph.

In the titanium-oxygen system, only one phase is stable in the composition range $TiO_{0.00}$ up to $TiO_{0.42}$ and this corresponds to the hexagonally close-packed lattice of titanium metal with oxygen atoms occupying interstitial positions. The lattice parameters of the metal are increased slightly as oxygen is taken up but the X-ray pattern remains essentially unchanged. Between the compositions $TiO_{0.42}$ and $TiO_{0.69}$ two phases separate out, one being titanium metal and the other the non-stoichiometric oxide described above which is the only stable phase in the composition range $TiO_{0.69}$ to $TiO_{1.33}$. It is surprising that the titanium atoms (and also the oxygen atoms) in this structure are in the arrangement of cubic close-packing in contrast to the hexagonal close-packing of the pure metal, in particular as the next stable phase, in the range $TiO_{1.46}$ to $TiO_{1.56}$, has the corundum structure which is based on hexagonal close-packing once again.

Another compound which is similar to titanium(II) oxide in being grossly defective at the stoichiometric composition is chromium(II) sulphide. This phase does not have such a wide stability range as the titanium oxide and is stable only in the metal-deficient direction.

Some Consequences of the Existence of Defects and Non-stoichiometry

It has already been pointed out earlier in this chapter that conduction by solids takes place by defect mechanisms. Some other properties of the solid state which are also explained by the existence of defects will now be described.

When an ionic solid is irradiated with light, most of the light is reflected, but with light of short wavelength, however, for example in the ultra-violet, some absorption occurs. The light energy causes an electron to become excited and removes it from an anion; it then becomes trapped in the vicinity of the anion and the site originally occupied by the electron becomes in consequence a positive hole. If the electron acquires sufficient energy from the light source, it becomes separated entirely from its environment and becomes mobile; it can then travel over the entire crystal lattice and can conduct an electric current. This is the phenomenon known as photoconductivity, the compound being rendered a conductor of electricity by the incidence of light radiation.

The energy acquired by the crystal can be given out again as thermal energy, but in some cases it is emitted as radiation of somewhat higher wavelength (and hence lower energy since some of the energy is always lost in other ways), than the incident radiation, when the compound is said to be luminescent.

Luminescence ceases when the source of light is removed, but in some cases an emission continues even after irradiation has ceased. Compounds which show this property are said to be phosphorescent, and in most such compounds the centres which are responsible for the phosphorescence are impurity atoms of different valence in the lattice which act as electron traps. The emission of radiation, which is the phosphorescence, continues after the removal of the light source because the process by which the compound returns to its ground state is a 'forbidden' one and does not take place instantaneously.

Perhaps the most commonly known luminous material is zinc sulphide, in which the impurity centres are thought to be neutral zinc atoms or, more frequently, copper ions added intentionally. Luminescence is produced not only by light but also by X-rays, positive ions, etc.; X-rays cause zinc sulphide to give off a green-blue luminescence and in consequence zinc sulphide screens are commonly used for the detection of X-ray sources. When zinc sulphide is mixed with an alpha-particle emitter, such as a radium compound, a permanent luminescence will result since the positively charged alpha-particles are being emitted all the time, and such a mixture is used for the numbers and hands of a 'luminous' watch.

As has been pointed out previously, when an alkali halide is heated in the vapour of the appropriate metal, it acquires a deep colour which is characteristic of the individual halide. This colour does not fade with time. If an alkali halide is exposed to ultra-violet light, X-radiation or bombardment with electrons, the same colour develops, but the colour so produced fades rapidly when the source of energy is removed. It has been established that the colour, irrespective of the way in which it is produced, is caused by electrons which are trapped in vacant anion sites. These vacant anion sites are effectively positively charged since they represent a deficiency in negative charge, and are able to attract electrons. An electron trapped in such a site is referred to as an F-centre, F being an abbreviation for farbe, the German word for colour.

In the non-stoichiometric crystal (Type I) as formed by the action of the metal vapour, the larger the number of metal atoms taken up the greater the number of trapped electrons and hence the more intense the colour. When the crystal develops colour on irradiation by X-rays, etc., there is no departure from stoichiometry and the electrons released on irradiation must be trapped in existing Schottky vacancies.

The photochemical changes in silver halides which are used in the photographic process must also involve defects in the structure, but reference should be made to a more advanced text-book for information on this subject.

Another aspect of the solid state which is of considerable chemical interest is the mechanism of solid-solid reactions. As soon as two solids which can react with each other are mixed under appropriate conditions the reaction product(s) are formed at the interface, and this means that the reactants are no longer in contact with each other; none the less, reaction can proceed to completion. The classical work of Wagner was of considerable importance in this field and some of these studies will be described here. Perhaps the best known is the so-called tarnishing reaction between silver and sulphur with formation of silver sulphide.

Wagner separated some sulphur from a block of silver by means of two slabs of silver sulphide and the system was heated for some time; the slabs were weighed separately before and after heating. The system is represented diagrammatically below.

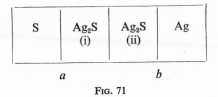

Fig. 71

Reaction can take place at the interface a if silver ions can migrate from b to a through the silver sulphide lattice, at interface b if sulphide ions can migrate from a to b, and at both interfaces if both types of ion can migrate. Reaction at a would lead to a gain in weight in slab (i) and at b in slab (ii). It was found experimentally that only slab (i) gained in weight so that reaction must have proceeded only at a, the sulphur-silver sulphide interface.

Ionisation of the silver must occur at b, the silver–silver sulphide interface, i.e. $2Ag \rightarrow 2Ag^+ + 2e^-$. Both the silver ions and the free electrons can then migrate through the solid silver sulphide by a defect mechanism, to react with sulphur at the sulphur-silver sulphide interface b, i.e. $2Ag^+ + S + 2e^- \rightarrow Ag_2S$. Silver sulphide normally conducts an electric current by an electronic mechanism so that such a passage of electrons through the crystal as is required in the above mechanism is a reasonable possibility.

A mechanism which involves the migration of ions only and not of electrons also is found in the formation of $\alpha\text{-}Ag_2HgI_4$ from silver and mercury(II) iodides. When blocks of the two metal iodides are separated by a block of the complex product and the system is heated to a temperature above 60° C., reaction proceeds with the formation of the complex at both interfaces. It is found that silver ions move through the block of the complex iodide in one direction and mercuric ions in the opposite direction in equivalent amounts. No electrons are involved as the metals are present as their ions in all the compounds used.

As a last example the reaction between metallic copper and solid silver chloride can be considered, $Cu + AgCl \rightarrow Ag + CuCl$; in this case there are two reaction products and the mechanism of this reaction is represented diagrammatically below. It is similar to that described for the

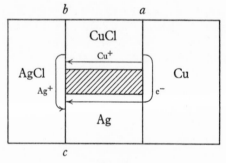

FIG. 72

tarnishing reaction above. At the copper-copper(I) chloride interface a ionisation of copper takes place, i.e. $Cu \rightarrow Cu^+ + e^-$. The copper ion then migrates through the solid copper(I) chloride lattice to b, where it replaces a silver ion in the silver chloride. The silver ion thus replaced migrates through the lattice of silver chloride to c, the silver-silver chloride interface, where it reacts with an electron to form a silver atom, i.e. $Ag^+ + e^- \rightarrow Ag$. The electron used in this reaction is that liberated at a which has travelled through the lattices of the metallic copper and silver to c. Thus the reaction involves the migration of metal ions and also of electrons.

Many metal oxides are important for their catalytic properties. Good evidence has been obtained recently for the belief that the electronic characteristics of the oxides play an important part in determining their catalytic efficiency; at some stage during a catalysed reaction, the reacting molecules are adsorbed on the surface of the catalyst and must therefore be influenced by its electrical field.

One of the reactions which has been most extensively studied from this point of view is the catalytic decomposition of nitrous oxide into its elements on oxide catalysts. When the oxides are arranged in order as their efficiency at catalysing the decomposition of nitrous oxide decreases, the following sequence is obtained:

p-type semi-conductors > insulators > n-type semi-conductors,

e.g. Cu_2O and NiO > MgO and Al_2O_3 > ZnO and CdO. The most efficient catalyst of all is copper(I) oxide.

A further demonstration that the availability of electrons or positive holes must influence catalytic activity is afforded by studying the effect of deliberate variation in the composition of a selected catalyst. The introduction of cations of charge $+1$ into the lattice of the p-type NiO enhances its catalytic activity, and it has been pointed out previously (p. 158) that such a variation in composition increases the number of positive holes. Similarly, the introduction of cations of charge $+3$ decreases both the catalytic activity and the number of positive holes.

Other reactions have also been studied with similar results, although it is not always found that the sequence is the same as that above. For example, it is found that insulators are less efficient than n-type semi-conductors in effecting the catalytic oxidation of carbon monoxide.

In view of the widespread occurrence of non-stoichiometry it is of interest to have second thoughts about some apparently obvious chemical ideas. According to the Law of Definite Proportions, a compound is absolutely fixed in its chemical composition by weight. Such a definition clearly can not apply to non-stoichiometric materials which can exist over a range of composition and yet it cannot be that every slight difference in composition represents a different compound, e.g. the case of TiO above. Such non-stoichiometric compounds always have the same crystal lattice even although there is a difference in the number of sites occupied, and they cannot be separated into more than one phase. As a result of having the same crystal lattice, different compositions still give rise to the same X-ray spectrum.

It is a strange twist of fate that when the schoolboy heats iron filings and sulphur together to demonstrate that he has produced a material which has different characteristics from those of his starting materials, i.e. a compound, he produces a material which can exist over a significant range of composition in apparent defiance of the Law of Definite Proportions, and which cannot exist with the ideal composition by which he represents the compound on paper! It is fortunate that early chemists based their researches on stoichiometric compounds or chemical knowledge would not be so far advanced as it is at the present day.

The purity of a non-stoichiometric compound is difficult to define. For example, to analyse FeS for its iron content alone would not be sufficient as the ratio of sulphur to iron is not constant. Only a complete analysis can give any information, and purity would presumably mean the presence of no elements other than iron and sulphur, coupled with an X-ray investigation to show that there were no other phases such as metallic iron or iron pyrites present in small amount.

Another difficulty is to define the oxidation state of the metal in such compounds as FeO and FeS. Although iron(II), or ferrous, predominates, a small and variable amount of iron(III), or ferric, is always present.

Finally, it can be appreciated easily that the choice of compound to be used in an equivalent weight determination, or as a precipitate in a gravimetric analysis must be made carefully. The use of a non-stoichiometric compound would be possible only in the unlikely event of its composition being constant and known. The difficulty of trying to determine the equivalent weight of titanium by combination with oxygen to form the monoxide with its widely varying composition can well be imagined.

Element	1st	2nd	3rd	4th	5th	6th	7th
Sn	7·3	14·5	30·5	39·4	80·7		
Sb	8·6	18·6	24·7	44·0	55·5		
Te	9·0	21·6	30·7	38·0	60·5		
I	10·4	19·1	31·5	41·8			
Xe	12·1	21·1					
Cs	3·9	23·4					
Ba	5·2	10·0					
La	5·6	11·4	19·2				
Hf	—						
Ta	—						
W	8·0						
Re	7·9						
Os	8·7						
Ir	9·2						
Pt	9·0	19·4					
Au	9·2	20·0					
Hg	10·4	18·7	34·3				
Tl	6·1	20·3	29·7	50·5			
Pb	7·4	15·0	32·2	42·1	69·4		
Bi	8·5	16·8	25·7	45·5	56·2		

APPENDIX III

Some Ionic Radii (after Goldschmidt)

Element	Charge	Radius (Å)
Li	+1	0·78
Be	+2	0·34
O	−2	1·33
F	−1	1·33
Na	+1	0·98
Mg	+2	0·78
Al	+3	0·57
Si	+4	0·39
S	−2	1·74
Cl	−1	1·81
K	+1	1·33
Ca	+2	1·06
Sc	+3	0·83
Ti	+4	0·64
Cr	+3	0·64
Mn	+2	0·91
Fe	+2	0·83
	+3	0·67
Co	+2	0·82
Ni	+2	0·78
Cu	+1	0·96
Zn	+2	0·83
Ga	+3	0·62
Ge	+4	0·44
Se	−2	1·91
Br	−1	1·96
Rb	+1	1·49
Sr	+2	1·27
Y	+3	1·06
Zr	+4	0·87
Ag	+1	1·13
Cd	+2	1·03
In	+3	0·92
Sn	+4	0·74
Te	−2	2·11
I	−1	2·20
Cs	+1	1·65
Ba	+2	1·43
La	+3	1·22
Ce	+4	1·02
	+3	1·18
Pr−Lu	+3	1·16−0·99
Hf	+4	0·84
Hg	+2	1·12
Tl	+1	1·49
Pb	+2	1·32
U	+4	1·05

BIBLIOGRAPHY

The following are suggestions for further reading; the list is not meant to be comprehensive.

Cartmell and Fowles (1956). *Valency and Molecular Structure*. Butterworth.

Evans (1952). *An Introduction to Crystal Chemistry*. Cambridge University Press.

Garner (1955). *Chemistry of the Solid State*. Butterworth.

Griffith and Orgel (1957). 'Ligand Field Theory', *Quarterly Reviews of the Chemical Society*, vol. XL, p. 381.

Hückel (1951). *Structural Chemistry of Inorganic Compounds*. Elsevier.

Moeller (1952). *Inorganic Chemistry*. John Wiley & Sons.

Nyholm and Gillespie (1957). 'Inorganic Stereochemistry', *Quarterly Reviews of the Chemical Society*, vol. XI, p. 339.

Orgel (1960). *An Introduction to Transition-Metal Chemistry*. Methuen.

Pauling (1959). *The Nature of the Chemical Bond*, 3rd Ed. Oxford.

Wells (1950). *Structural Inorganic Chemistry*, 2nd Ed. Oxford.

Wheatley (1959). *Determination of Molecular Structure*. Oxford.

FORMULA INDEX

Reference is made to an element or compound in this Index only when the appropriate structure is given. Certain mineral silicates are included (in a section at the end) by name only on account of the complexity of their formulae.

SUBJECT INDEX